D0262766

Talking Cures:
a guide to the
psychotherapies
for health care professionals

Philip J Barker PhD RN FRCN

Dedication

To Poppy, for teaching me the meaning of presence.

Names of patients in case studies have been changed.

First published 1999 by Nursing Times Books
Emap Healthcare Ltd, part of Emap Business Communications
Greater London House
Hampstead Road
London NW1 7EJ

Text © 1999 P J Barker

Cover artwork: Senate Design Ltd, London SW15 1AZ

Printed and bound in Great Britain by Drogher Press, Christchurch, Dorset

British Library cataloguing in Publication Data
A catalogue record for this book is available from the British Library.

ISBN: 1 902499 10 7

Contents

Contributors

Kate Bones
Head Occupational Therapist
Camden and Islington Community Mental Health Team
London, England

Jon Chesterson
Nurse Educator (Mental Health)
Centre for Professional Development
Canberra Hospital
Canberra, Australia

Sue Croom
Senior Lecturer/Practitioner
University of Northumbria and Newcastle City Health Trust
Newcastle Upon Tyne, England

Ann Garland
Research Associate
Department of Psychiatry
University of Newcastle
England

Una Hunt
CPN
Camden and Islington Community Mental Health Team
London, England

Cordt Kassner
Psychiatric Research Coordinator
University of Colorado Health Sciences Center
Denver, USA

Richard Lakeman
Senior Lecturer
Department of Nursing
Eastern Institute of Technology
Hawke's Bay, New Zealand

Tony MacCulloch
Counsellor and Group Facilitator
School of Nursing
Health Studies Faculty
Auckland Institute of Technology
Auckland, New Zealand

Dr Martin Teising
Professor of Nursing
University of Applied Sciences
Fachhocschule Frankfurt
Frankfurt, Germany

Mark Radcliffe
Mental Health Editor
Nursing Times
London, England

Kay Vaughn
Clinical Nurse Specialist
University of Colorado Health Sciences Centre
Denver, USA

Denise Webster
Professor
University of Colorado Health Sciences Center
Denver, USA

Ron Wilgosh
Barking, Havering and Brentwood
  Community Health Care Trust
Essex, England

Foreword

There is no doubting the impact that psychotherapy has had on modern culture. It has become a tool for those seeking health, an industry for those wanting happiness, an ideology for those wanting to think about themselves without being called self-indulgent, and a theory of knowledge that manages to describe and interpret the world – allegedly.

This suggests that for a lot of people, psychotherapy doesn't really mean anything terribly specific anymore. It has become interchangeable with the word counselling. It is an umbrella term for ways of 'talking helpfully' with someone in a systematic way, and in some quarters it has become a term of abuse for anyone who tries to have a conversation extending beyond your favourite soap opera.

When I first started nursing, I quickly developed doubts about psychotherapy. It seemed to me that it was only available to certain groups of patients. The middle-class ones, deemed to be eloquent and blessed with insight (or perhaps money), were often case-load patients for doctors doing their psychotherapy training. Less articulate, less 'interesting' patients with severe and enduring problems got drugs and little else. I, a student struggling for a view, was suspicious of what appeared to be the acceptable face of prejudice. Can it be that things were "oh, so simple" then?

Such cynicism, like a lot of cynicism, was helpful for a while (if ultimately self-defeating). Talking with people, any people, is so much more appealing than drugging them. So I, like most people, tried to talk and listen helpfully. I didn't have a system or a theory or anything. Still, whatever psychotherapy appeared to be, it wasn't for me. I didn't like its knowingness. I found it smug. I didn't like the amount of assumptions it made or its jargon – they were smug too. And mostly, as I came to read more about psychotherapy and listen to therapists talk about it, I wondered if perhaps the subject of psychotherapy was neither the patient, nor the process of communication, so much as the therapist, which struck me as plainly ridiculous. Psychotherapy made me itch.

Of course, it did eventually occur to me that psychotherapy had in fact become an umbrella term to me for all the obnoxious, self-indulgent and patronising nonsense I had seen issuing from people I didn't like or respect, but who worked in mental health. To be honest, this probably amounted to a nurse, two doctors and a handful of social workers. But who knows – I may have been in denial.

Now, more than a dozen years on, I've worked through my distaste for psychotherapy, in the main. I still don't trust people who call themselves psychotherapists, but Rome wasn't built in a day.

There are, of course, many different schools of therapy – different ways of talking with people who are experiencing profound distress, different ways of understanding problems and potential solutions – and goodness knows, those schools have been a little tribal in the past. I have been present at discussions where one type of therapist claimed a supremacy over another based on the length and expense of the qualification he had procured for himself. Five years of thrice-weekly analysis, sitting lots of exams, reading really dull books – and still they resort to a 'mine's bigger then yours' approach to debate. These are not people I'm going to share my problems with.

Personally, all the different schools of thought rather drifted over my head for quite a few years. I think I mistrusted them, and they didn't think much of me, as far as I can remember. As time went on, I, like absolutely everyone else, found my own style of working had evolved. This style (for want of a better word) owed more to my personality (for want of a better word) than any theory of understanding. I learnt from practitioners I admired, from teachers and patients, and, most importantly, from how I found myself feeling about what I was doing.

I retain the belief that most practitioners develop their style of practice in a broadly similar way: who they are influences their practice more profoundly than what they know. But who they are also tends to determine which kind of knowledge they pursue; and all clinicians, in one way or another, pursue greater understanding.

Each of the therapies discussed in this book reflects a distinct philosophical tradition. From the resolution of unconscious conflict at the heart of psychoanalysis (which formed the visionary basis of half of the critical theory that has emerged in the 20th century), to the post-modernism that attaches itself to solution-focused therapy (and has helped dispose of about 60% of the critical theory that emerged in the 20th century).

Arguably, this is the most important book that can be written about the practice of mental healthcare, and it is long overdue – an intelligent, informative overview of the major talking therapies in practice today; a theoretical and developmental history that is accessible and comprehensive; and with case studies to boot! For goodness sake, if you don't learn something very helpful from this book, you are either very very clever or quite dead. Certainly, every student of mental health practice – nurses, occupational therapists, doctors and social workers, should read it, regardless of what they believe or know.

Of course, there is so much to learn now: nursing models, medicine, protocols and assessment tools, research methods, professionalism and simple communication. But when it comes to the substance of working with people with mental health problems the way we use ourselves to help remains the core of clinical practice.

Away from the industry and the ideologues and the profiting (and the sarcasm), in actually working with people with severe, enduring or disabling difficulties, talking and listening with skill is the defining quality of a mental health practitioner. It took me ages to find a talking therapy that suited me. And because of my limitations, prejudices and politics, I seemingly barred myself from understanding fully the way other people worked and developed their practice. *I* could have done with this book. I imagine that, as a defensive and opinionated soul (though always polite), I would have read it critically, but I would indeed have learnt much.

Finally, I don't know if it is the job of a foreword to review the book. I assume not, but there are a couple of things worth highlighting. Firstly, the case studies, gathered from around the world and clearly written by very good practitioners, offer insight and clarity into the activity of therapy. This really should happen more, I think. There is sometimes a tendency in health texts to try to abstract meaning from an activity to form a theory – forgetting that the point of nursing theory is to inform activity. This book informs the activity of therapy. Secondly, the tone of the book – an even-handed curiosity for each school – is not just a testament to the editor, but also an example of the clarity, respect and openness that characterises good mental health work.

Mark Radcliffe

February 1999

Preface

Just about everyone knows something about psychotherapy. The influence of the cinema, television and the modern novel has encouraged even those who have never been near 'the couch', to be aware of *psychoanalysis*, and even those not naturally disposed to 'disclose' to have a feel for *counselling*. Such vicarious knowledge is born, especially, of watching Woody Allen, who reminds us that we all have human foibles, but perhaps only the wealthy New Yorker spends five hours a week free-associating on them. Many of our ideas about psychotherapy – what it is, what it is for and how useful it is – are probably just a little distorted. We may lack actual knowledge of the breadth of the psychotherapy field, ending up speaking in relative ignorance. Alternatively, we may favour one form of psychotherapy over others to such an extent that our hearts might, literally, be ruling our heads. Some of us may even want forms of psychotherapy that either do not exist, or that are not accessible.

Recently, a woman was admitted to an acute psychiatric ward, where she refused resolutely to talk to the nursing team, which was keen to assess her. After four days, one of the nurses brought in the psychiatrist to see her, and she spoke for the first time. She had been waiting – in her words – 'on the doctor to come with his couch'. The fact that psychiatrists neither carried portable couches nor, as a rule, did many of them do much in the way of psychotherapy, far less psychoanalysis, appeared to have escaped her. Her idea of a psychiatric unit, and her hopes for the kind of service she might receive in it, were framed perhaps more by the media than the realities of the health service.

And yet, perhaps many members of the public retain a need for the all-knowing psychiatric confessor, complete with couch. The expectation that a truly wise person (woman or man) will come to heal our mental hurt is timeless: threaded across all cultures and societies, ancient and modern, primitive and developed. The mental healing that takes place on the analyst's couch or in the counsellor's chair finds echoes in the meeting halls of modern faith healers and other 'miracle men', at the holy shrines of Ancient Greece and Judea, and in the thatched huts of the witch doctor or shaman. For mental healing not only signifies the resolution of mental illness, but suggests a search for human wholeness that extends far beyond the consulting rooms of the psychiatric ward and its associated clinics. As the world becomes more complex, and life becomes less certain, more and more of us seek security in the illusion that there is a whole retinue of soul doctors waiting to help us climb onto our couches, to free-associate our way towards peace and happiness. I hope the reader will find in this book examples of how we have extended the range of the practice – which might be called "mental healing: the methods" – while not losing sight of some of the core constituents of that healing process i.e. how we do it.

Our need for mental healing is part of the history of humanity. However, our pursuit of happiness, and desire to escape anxiety, has helped create the history of the development of modern psychotherapy – especially the psychotherapies of the past 40 years. Growing up in a working class family in a poor but proud Scottish community in the 1950s, I heard whispers about people who disappeared for months, sometimes years on end, only to reappear like 'shadows of their former selves' after a spell in the psychiatric hospital. These were usually women who found the struggle to live, and perhaps the absence of love, too hard to bear. Their treatment was usually barbiturates and ECT. If their menfolk could not face the struggle that fate had dealt them, they drank to oblivion and, in some cases, to death. There was much talking, but not much in the way of a 'talking cure', since a psychotherapy for the poor and inarticulate was not yet in common currency. My parents never understood what psychotherapy was and, although they knew that their son practised psychotherapy, it remained something beyond their ken. Although I would gradually gain some expertise in all five of the domains of psychotherapy described in this book, for many people of my parents' generation and background, this was simply more of the same: helping people who were 'bothered with their nerves'.

When I last went back, that small town was much bigger than I remembered and, although superficially more affluent, there appeared also to have been a corresponding growth in soul sickness. However, more people were talking about their 'needs' and some even appeared to have discovered the value of sharing them in some formal 'therapeutic' way. This extended even to some of the men who, as in other dying working-class communities, are almost an endangered species. Whether they will receive the kind of 'talking cures' they need in the measures required is, however, quite a different question.

This picture is true of the modern Westernised world at large. However, for most people, the psychological defences against 'opening up' and the cultural barriers to 'talking out' will be so great that many continue to resort to drink and drugs as temporary, and ineffective, cures for the affliction of their souls. A significant number of others will take more direct and dramatic action to end their misery. A hazardous guess is frequently made as to the economic cost of such human misery. The emotional cost of the same misery is so great that our usual reaction is to turn away, or to turn out yet more cold and unsatisfying statistics.

The word *psychotherapy* itself is enough to stimulate great defensiveness, not least in the form of ridicule and caricature. Of course, the therapist or counsellor is an easy target as a figure of fun, but that may merely be yet another reflection of our need for them, something we find hard to bear. However, a new voice of rejection has recently joined that of the comic or satirist: the researcher. For almost 50 years, ever since since Eysenck's infamous accusation that two thirds of psychotherapy patients recovered spontaneously, researchers have tried to evaluate the relative utility of various forms of psychotherapy. Over that same period, the number of methods and schools of psychotherapy have grown, literally into the hundreds. The demand for psychotherapy grows unabated, as the researchers – closely followed by health economists and politicians – continue to demand evidence of their effectiveness.

Counselling was a late child in the psychotherapy family, and is the latest form of therapy to attract the kind of dismissal that Eysenck reserved for psychoanalysis and psychodynamic therapies a half century ago. It is noted increasingly, and with more and more conviction, that "counselling doesn't work". This appears to mean either that 'counselling' encompasses such a wide range of methods it is difficult to define it, or that counselling is so ill-defined in practice, that it is difficult to collect evidence of its achievements. Recently, at a conference, I heard a woman talk powerfully about her experience of great mental distress, of hospitalisation and the often inept responses of healthcare professionals to her plight. She took time to consider the criticisms of counselling by academics and researchers, especially the effectiveness argument. She also noted how people with more serious forms of mental illness had been shown in a large research study to favour counselling and other forms of 'talking treatment'. She gave a light laugh as she noted that "if people want it, this in itself is evidence that counselling works". She was right, of course. Demand is a very powerful form of evidence, although not necessarily the same kind of evidence that a researcher or politician seeks to prove the efficacy of this or that kind of intervention. I shall say little about the formal evaluation of the many forms of therapy, which are related to the five main schools outlined in this book. I shall emphasise more the practice of psychotherapy, and how we might come to *judge* – rather than prove – whether or not psychotherapy appears to have met someone's need for mental healing.

As we tour through the main schools of psychotherapeutic thought, more emphasis will be given to identifying the elements that appear to unite all the psychotherapies. The capacity of the therapist to express compassion – that most ubiquitous form of love between people – is one such uniting element. Something that has long been seen as an important part of the process of change, but which, given its invisibility, makes formal evaluation of therapy difficult, if not impossible.

This book is aimed at all healthcare professionals interested in the psychotherapeutic dimensions of their work. It is not only those who disport themselves as 'therapists', of whatever persuasion, who might be found, in practice, to be 'therapeutic'. Ironically, often those who define themselves, specifically, as therapists end up being distinctly unhelpful and those who believe they offer only a 'listening ear' end up with the highest number of therapeutic votes. Some of that mysterious 'helpfulness' may have much to do with the capacity for compassion, and various other aspects of the relationship between therapist and patient, often are called the 'non-specific variables'. The importance of such characteristics of the therapist, and their relationship to the execution of the method, will be explored in some detail in the five sections of the book.

Although there will always be a demand, and need, for highly specialised therapy, the state of the post-modern Western world suggests that we shall never have enough specialist therapists. Indeed, all of us might benefit from an appreciation of how we might help others, and perhaps also ourselves, through engagement in the therapeutic process. This book is not aimed specifically at therapists – they already know what they are doing and why. Neither is this book aimed at people who want to become specialist therapy practitioners – although it may well help them decide whether or not such a career is appropriate or realistic for them, and perhaps what kind of psychotherapy attracts them. This text aims, more modestly, at clarifying the process, usefulness and appropriate application of therapy, for a wide audience of healthcare professionals. Such ambitions are modest but important. I hope to help readers appreciate:

- what therapy might be all about, at some fundamental level;
- how it has been translated into a number of key therapeutic languages;
- how their own work might possess an important therapeutic dimension, and, more importantly, how readers might develop their psychotherapeutic potential.

I look out on my beloved estuary as I write this preface, the sharp winter light framing the whole landscape in a steely gaze. Despite the chill, the birds continue to sing as they engage in the endless task of feeding and repairing nests. Perhaps they sing because they have not lost the balance between love and work – the balance that, for Freud, was the essence of happiness: two fast-receding qualities, in an increasingly steely human landscape. Perhaps theirs is a song of hope, or at least a muffled reminder that the instillation of hope is a central ambition of any psychotherapy. We are hoping, perhaps, for more love and more work.

I can also hear the voices of the many people who have helped me to be able to sit down to write this book, although their voices are embedded within me. I could not end this preface without thanking my many mentors, who helped me to develop my limited therapeutic skills; and the countless numbers of people who – as patients – helped me grow my compassion and extend my empathy. With their help, I have trodden a long, fascinating and – I believe – ultimately enlightening path over the past 30 years. I cannot say with any confidence that I *really* know about psychotherapy, but I am now much more confident about what I do not know, and that 'negative knowledge' always seemed to serve some useful purpose. If readers come only to develop their own 'therapeutic doubt', then my purpose in preparing this text will have been realised.

Phil Barker
Newport-on-Tay, Scotland

1. The healing of the mind: meaning and method

THE ORIGINS OF PSYCHOTHERAPY

In its proper sense, *psychotherapy* means 'mental healing' – stemming from the Greek for mind (psyche) and Latin for healing (therapia). Although I shall emphasise the history of psychotherapy, beginning with its late modern roots in Freud's psychoanalysis, 'mental healing' stretches back to ancient history, through philosopher-priests to the medicine man and magician. That ancient and cross-cultural history is important, since the effectiveness of psychotherapy – *why* and *how* it works – still has much in common with the ideas of the philosophers of religion and the interpersonal skills of the shaman. Indeed, magical, religious and scientific viewpoints still influence the development of late 20th century psychotherapies, and are simply three different ways of looking at the same thing – the *mental distress* that we seek to heal.

In this era of evidence-based healthcare, there is a growing desire to know what works and why. The desire to understand mental healing, in a scientific sense, began with Freud over a century ago, and continues today with various attempts to analyse and evaluate the interpersonal processes of helping people in mental distress, through the power of conversation – the talking cure.

WHAT IS PSYCHOTHERAPY?

The *practice* of psychotherapy is more helpful than any dictionary in finding a suitable definition, since it reveals what can be done in the name of *helping*. These practices range from listening, advising, guiding, educating and even influencing the patient[1]. Although originally associated with the practice of psychiatric medicine, psychotherapy has become increasingly associated with psychology, nursing and social casework and, in various forms of counselling, has become – increasingly – a lay discipline in its own right.

Although disputes between differing schools continue, the following definition of psychotherapy might gain general approval:

> Psychotherapy involves the psychological treatment of problems of living, by a trained person, within the context of a professional relationship, involving either removing, reducing or modifying specific emotional, cognitive or behavioural problems; and/or promoting social adaption, personality development and/or personal growth.

The range of techniques that might be employed in such a 'psychological treatment' is virtually limitless, ranging across individual, couple, group and family therapies.

All are, however, dependent on some form of interpersonal communication – a conversation between therapist and patient.

Although the focus of psychotherapy may take various forms – feelings, thoughts or disturbing patterns of behaviour – in general, such problems result in some problem of living[2], which distresses the person, others or both. Psychotherapy requires a highly specific relationship, between patient and therapist, which, unlike ordinary relationships, emphasises a collaborative undertaking, geared toward the attainment of specific therapeutic objectives.

Some forms of psychotherapy are problem-specific, aiming only to reduce distress, or promote a limited form of social adaption. Other therapies, especially within the humanistic school, are concerned more with the development of the personality: freeing patients from limiting ways of thinking, feeling or behaving that restrict the expression of their full humanity. These represent a break from the tradition of therapy as a narrow, medicalised treatment of mental or nervous disorders. Although the utility of traditional forms of psychotherapy is difficult to evaluate, at face value most problem-oriented therapies appear to meet their goal of reducing distress. The extent to which the humanistic, and especially the transpersonal, therapies (see Epilogue) represent a viable alternative to such traditional models remains in doubt. This may have something to do with the all-encompassing, often spiritual, issues, which such forms of therapy address.

PSYCHOTHERAPY AND PSYCHOANALYSIS

Although most dictionary definitions include psychoanalysis as one of the psychotherapies, this is misleading. Psychoanalysis involves a systematic and total resolution of unconscious conflicts and, as a result, requires structural alteration of defences and character organisation (Wolberg, 1995). This is an ambitious undertaking, requiring a major investment of commitment and time on the part of therapist and patient. By contrast, psychotherapy appears less ambitious, seeking more practical goals, resolving discrete problems, perhaps even encouraging the retention of certain problematic patterns (such as neurotic defenses) to allow the person to function effectively. This is not to suggest that psychoanalysis occupies some kind of 'higher ground', or is in any way 'better' than psychotherapy. Given the ambitions of formal psychoanalysis, a stringent selection procedure operates: certain personality and motivational characteristics are required, not to mention time and (usually) money. As a result, relatively few people are appropriate for analysis, whereas just about anyone can be considered for some form of psychotherapy.

In establishing psychoanalysis, Freud laid the basis for a highly specific 'school' which required strict observance on the part of its followers. In particular he maintained, to the end of his life, that no one could be an analyst who did not accept the foundation of the theory of psychoanalysis. This meant that an analyst would accept the existence of unconscious mental processes, the theory of repression and resistance and, perhaps most importantly, the importance of sexuality and the Oedipus complex (Freud, 1952). Although various splinter groups have developed within traditional psychoanalysis, it remains a form of human helping quite distinct from the psychotherapies discussed in this text. However, perhaps as an indirect function of Freud's rigid position, there has emerged a psychoanalytic, or dynamic, psychotherapy that accepts some, but not all, of Freud's original premises. The position of psychoanalysis, as a preferred method of treatment, belongs to the past. However, this does not mean that its importance, as a form of influence or means of helping us understand how psychotherapy works, has lessened. Indeed, 'psychoanalytically-oriented' or 'psycho-dynamic' psychotherapy has become, arguably, the most common form of psychotherapy worldwide.

WHAT ARE THE MAIN VARIETIES OF PSYCHOTHERAPY?

The scope of this book prohibits any more than a brief overview of some of the main classes of psychotherapy and their application. The number of practices described as 'psychotherapy' presently runs into hundreds. Almost 20 years ago, as many as 250 different therapies were listed (Herink, 1980; Corsini, 1981), although many enjoyed a short-lived prominence, only to fade back into obscurity. I shall discuss five main groups: psychoanalytic, behavioural, humanistic, family and solution-focused. I begin here, however, with a consideration of the three main *functions* of all these therapies.

The three main functions of the psychotherapies

The sheer complexity of the psychotherapy field – with its dozens of 'schools' and hundreds of splinter groups – can cause great confusion. There is a growing feeling that 'everything works or nothing works', a realisation hatched from apocryphal tales of someone's failure to benefit from traditional therapy, but miraculous improvements after two sessions of some 'new age' therapy. In later chapters, I shall consider which problems of living (and patients) might best be addressed by different therapies. Here, I consider briefly what might be the three core functions, upon which all forms of psychotherapy might be based:

1. Support

Most people who come for therapy[3] experience distress, which they wish to be reduced, if not eliminated. Such patients want their emotional equilibrium restored, perhaps through developing their sense of control over their circumstances.

Supportive forms of psychotherapy emphasise discrete, even narrow, objectives: helping the person to strengthen their existing defences, gaining some kind of security that will allow them to deal with their difficulties. To provide such support, the therapist offers four main responses to the patient's problems:

▷ *Offering guidance and reassurance:* encouraging the patient to accept some aspects of her/his experience, while 'normalising' others;

▷ *Facilitating emotional catharsis:* allowing or encouraging the patient to express feelings;

▷ *Promoting self-esteem:* helping to identify and clarify personal assets or resources;

▷ *Enabling coping responses:* helping the person manage specific problems – through hypnosis, training in deep muscle relaxation, or encouraging group membership to allow additional support and peer-identification.

2. Re-education

Other patients either request or need to make some change in their lives. This may involve fulfilling their creative potential – including their capacity to deal with some problem – or adjusting their goals for everyday living. Such objectives may involve changes within the person, their relationships with others, or both.

Re-educative forms of psychotherapy emphasise making deliberate efforts at re-adjustment. Reaching these goals may, or may not, require that the patient develop insight into the conscious conflicts. A wide range of highly divergent therapies might be offered to help this re-educative process. Depending on the nature of the main presenting problem of living, any of the following might be indicated:

▷ *Behaviour or conditioning therapy*: for specific patterns of problematic behaviour;

▷ *Client-centred therapy*: developing the patient's self-awareness;

▷ *Rational-emotive therapy*: focusing on self-defeating beliefs;

▷ *Marital or family therapy*: addressing specific relationship difficulties;

▶ *Cognitive therapy*: focusing on dysfunctional styles of thinking and acting;

▶ *Psychodrama*: developing awareness of some specific event, through re-enactment;

▶ *Philosophic therapy* (for example, existential or Zen Buddhist): setting problems of living within a wider frame of spiritual reference.

3. Reconstruction

Finally, some people desire, or need, to address their problems of living at a more deep-seated level, aiming to develop insight into unconscious conflicts, making discrete changes to their character structure, or expanding their personality through the development, for them, of some new-found 'human potential'.

Reconstructive therapy implies the need to go deeper into the personality structure. Most, although not all, of the approaches used to accomplish this will be psychoanalytic in form. As noted above, there now exists a great range of 'schools' of analysis – from traditional Freudian psychoanalysis, through various neo-Freudian approaches, to various psychoanalytical-oriented psychotherapies, including transactional analysis, existential analysis and group analysis. These approaches may be supplemented by hypnosis or adjunct drug therapy (especially sedation), play therapy in the case of children, and art therapy, to help express material that is somehow 'beyond words'.

COUNSELLING AND PSYCHOTHERAPY

Although now used interchangeably, once there were distinct differences between counselling and psychotherapy. In counselling, patients (usually called 'clients')[4] were helped to understand themselves better, so that they might take some action to remedy or resolve some social or adjustment difficulty. This process was usually short term and focused on specific difficulties in the 'here and now' of the patient's experience. Traditionally, counsellors offered suggestions as to available resources, and actively interpreted the patient's feelings and attitudes. Counselling in that form served a supportive function: the counsellor adopted the position of an authority, helping patients to help themselves, through evaluating problems and possible courses of action. Psychotherapy had more complex ambitions, addressing more complex issues, involving either re-education or reconstruction. The psychotherapist adopted a much less directive function and the goals were much longer term.

With the development of Rogers' non-directive counselling (Rogers, 1942), the differences between psychotherapy and counselling became blurred. Rogers advocated a careful facilitation of the expression of feelings by the client, within a supportive relationship. The emphasis was, however, on the client undertaking most of the 'work'. The counsellor was to reflect back key phrases of emotional expression, to help clarify their form and function. This was aimed at helping clients to assume responsibility for their feelings and to consider what they needed to do next to address their life problems.

One could take the view that counselling focuses on resolving specific, situational problems, whereas psychotherapy addresses broader problems – such as personality or esteem difficulties – that result in situational crises. Although such a definition is workable in the areas of, for example, vocational or educational counselling, practitioners talk increasingly of counselling the bereaved, the dying and others with complex emotional, behavioural and even spiritual problems. At the same time, some forms of psychotherapy – such as behavioural psychotherapy – can be highly specific, aiming to resolve specific emotional or behavioural problems, and no more.

For purely pragmatic reasons, I shall use the terms counselling and psychotherapy interchangeably, recognising that their emphasis will differ mainly according to their supportive, re-educative or reconstructive functions.

THE CHARACTERISTICS AND ROLE OF THE THERAPIST

All psychotherapy takes place within the context of a highly specific relationship, and certain characteristics of the therapist, and how therapy is undertaken, play a significant part in its success or failure. The five main therapeutic features exhibited are:

1. Good authority

When patients enter therapy, they are likely to be demoralised, distraught or otherwise 'suffering'. The therapist's primary responsibility is to establish a relationship within which the patient may feel sufficiently secure to begin addressing the problem brought to therapy. This principle applies whatever the aims: supportive, re-educative or reconstructive. Essentially, patients put their destiny in the hands of someone whom they hope will be understanding, protective, non-punitive and helpful. These are the essential qualities of the 'good authority' patients expect will be presiding over the therapeutic process. The greater the distress experienced by the patient, the more likely that the therapist will be idealised as a parent (authority) figure. The nature of this power dynamic – with the therapist very much in charge (control) and the patient dependent on support and approval – can represent a challenge for the therapist, especially the risk of abusing such power. Some therapists intentionally develop the power-dynamic with the patient (especially psychoanalytic therapists), while others try to reduce this, making the relationship more equal and balanced (especially cognitive therapists). However, the differential in power between patient and therapists is central to all psychotherapy. Indeed, by virtue of their expectation that the therapist will be helpful, patients project power (and authority) on to their therapist. However, the fundamental, and powerful, nature of this union allows the therapist to restore the patient's morale and represents the core function of all the psychotherapies (Frank, 1974).

2. Communication

Therapy is no more than a conversation, developed within the core relationship. Here, the therapist tries to help the patient grow in understanding, regarding the nature of the problem. This requires the therapist to be able to communicate in terms that are not only understandable to the patient – using her/his own language – but also acceptable, given the stage of development reached. In addition to knowing what to tell the patient, and how to frame this, the therapist needs to know when this would be appropriate, and also when it would be appropriate to say nothing.

3. Direction

Even when the therapist is helping the patient to establish the meaning of certain experiences, chart her/his own course or determine what actions need to be taken, direction is being provided. Ironically, even by being 'non-directive', the therapist provides direction. Such direction is expected, since if patients were able to work out things for themselves, they would not be in therapy.

4. Encouragement

The therapist also serves as a source of encouragement, helping patients become aware of progress, reinforcing their independent decision-making, and helping them to stay focused on dealing with problems and issues, which they might otherwise wish to turn away from.

5. Safe space

In most forms of psychotherapy, patients need to reflect on attitudes, values or beliefs – about themselves or others – which they have long held; and consider their origins and possible alternative ways of construing the world. This involves people looking (metaphorically) at themselves in a 'full-length mirror', perhaps even 'naked'. Patients can only undertake such challenging personal work successfully when they have reached a certain stage in the relationship. Time limits cannot be put on this: it may take a few sessions, or it may take many more. However, this 'safe space' grows out of the good authority with which the relationship began, and represents, also, a crucial stage in the closure of the relationship.

TRUST, FAITH AND THE EXPECTATION OF CHANGE

These 'therapeutic gifts' are found in all effective therapy. Indeed, they represent the processes that operate in all human helping, whether or not called psychotherapy. Carl Rogers attached a new set of terms to some of the dimensions of the therapeutic relationship, emphasising the need for warmth, empathy, genuineness and unconditional positive regard. These apparently simple characteristics of the therapist's orientation towards the patient provide the basis for the restoration of basic trust, which is the foremost task of psychotherapy (Strupp, 1972).

Not all therapists emphasise the importance of the relationship to the same extent, some suggesting that the relationship merely supports the application of specific psychotherapy techniques. This view is often favoured by behavioural or cognitive psychotherapists (for example, Newell and Dryden, 1991). For other therapists, the relationship is central. What produces the results is the dedication of the therapist to a specific system, "his [sic] sincerity of purpose and the transmission of the message to the patient that the therapist 'cares' about what happens to him" (Rogers, 1961).

These relationship factors influence the operation of faith – the extent to which the therapist believes in his chosen method, and the extent to which he can encourage the patient to join him. Such faith in the therapeutic system can result in therapy working, literally 'like a charm'. All forms of therapy – physical and psychological – possess placebo properties. The patient's belief in the method, or the therapist's strong 'selling' of the method, produce effects that may have nothing to do with the method itself. Here, modern therapy harkens back to the power of the shaman: the magic of the psychotherapist is still an important part of the therapeutic process.

Today, there is great emphasis on trying to establish what specific processes in psychotherapy account for specific outcomes. What does the therapist do that produces specific change in the patient's presentation? It appears, at present, that rather than any one thing, or even collection of things, it is more how the therapist orchestrates the therapeutic process that determines a good result.

AN OVERVIEW OF THE THERAPEUTIC PROCESS

The therapeutic process has four main stages: a beginning, two central stages and a conclusion. Although an analysis of effective therapy will invariably show these stages, they are rarely discrete, and much overlap occurs between them.

In the beginning stage, the therapist focuses on establishing the working alliance with the patient. This involves:

▶ Encouraging the patient to join therapy;

▶ Explaining what will happen in the therapy process;

▶ Showing understanding of the patient's plight and promoting an appreciation that the therapist will be of some help in addressing this;

▶ Encouraging a preliminary statement of the aims (goals) of the therapy.

In the first of the central stages, the therapist explores the background to the patient's problems and their present consequences in everyday life. This involves:

▶ Exploring the patient's relationship with the problem – seeking to clarify particular thoughts, feelings and actions that are, in some way, connected to the problem.

How that 'connection' is explored, is determined by the therapist's chosen method. For example, psychoanalytic therapists will probe for unconscious conflicts, through use of, for example, free association or dream interpretation; cognitive therapists will look for signs of self-defeating thoughts, which might precipitate negative feelings; and behaviour therapists will attempt to identify the specific factors that appear to reinforce dysfunctional patterns of behaviour.

In the second central stage, the therapist begins the process of translating the patient's understanding of the problem into action for change, correction of forward movement. Again, a range of options is possible, depending on the method of therapy used. The therapist might:

▶ Review incentives for change;

▶ Help the patient manage specific emotional disturbance;

▶ Focus on forces that appear to block the process of change;

▶ Encourage the expression of powerful emotions (catharsis);

▶ Help the patient reconcile her/himself to situations that are beyond control.

In the final, or termination, stage, the therapist draws both the process of therapy and the relationship to a conclusion. Although the patient may have made great strides during the previous three stages, here both have to address the complex issue of 'life beyond therapy'. All therapists have to address similar problems:

▶ How can the patient bring a necessarily 'dependent' relationship to an end, with minimum emotional trauma?

▶ How can they assist the patient to take full ownership of the problem, and the continuing work necessary to maintain or develop progress in addressing it?

▶ How can they promote the patient's independence and emotional assertiveness, beyond therapy?

These three stages present all therapists – but especially the novice – with great challenges. In the beginning stage, therapists often find it difficult to relate appropriately to the patient, becoming either irritated by the patient's apparent inability to respond, or lacking any sense of sympathy (far less empathy) for the patient's predicament. Alternatively, therapists may show too much concern, swamping patients with concern and compassion, making them unnecessarily dependent. Rogers' ideal of "non-possessive warmth" can be difficult to judge.

In the central stages, the therapist may avoid addressing patients' problems that, perhaps unconsciously, stimulate anxiety in the therapist. Alternatively, the therapist may probe too deeply into issues that concern the therapist, but that are not really important to the patient. Again, the patient's 'slowness' or 'resistance' may irritate the therapist, or alternatively, the therapist may do too much work, further increasing the dependency of the patient.

In the termination stage, the therapist may find it difficult to 'let go' of the patient. At the conclusion, the parting may be difficult for both therapist and patient, and the therapist may tend to underestimate the patient's capacity for independence, or alternatively may try to push an ill-prepared patient into a potentially dangerous state of independence.

THERAPEUTIC ASSIGNMENTS

Although most therapists encouraged patients to 'work' on their problems, between sessions, the idea of the formal 'homework assignment', is fairly recent (Ellis,1962). Assignments became popular within cognitive and behavioural psychotherapies, but now are found in almost all approaches, especially those employing some kind of self-management. The range of assignments is virtually limitless, but assignments usually emphasise the independent management of the problems that brought the patient to therapy. In most cases, patients are encouraged to keep daily logs, or diaries, recording their thoughts, feelings and actions, and this format may provide the basis for projecting into the future, developing the resolution of the problem.

Patients are usually given an assignment that is related directly to the current work of the session. This may be highly specific or might be more diffuse. Among the many classic 'diffuse' assignments are the following practice assignments:

- Let go of the past;

- Tolerate a certain amount of anxiety;

- Tolerate a certain degree of hostility;

- Tolerate a certain degree of irritation, frustration or deprivation;

- Make a small change to your environment, that is for the better;

- Identify something that cannot be changed and accept it;

- Use your will power to stop engaging in some destructive activity;

- Challenge one negative view of yourself;

- Select a pleasurable activity from a list and engage in it;

- Make more reasonable demands on yourself;

- Accept the responsibilities of your social role, one by one.

THE RELEVANCE OF PSYCHOTHERAPY FOR HEALTHCARE PROFESSIONALS

The death-knell for the 'talking cure' has been sounded for at least 50 years, since Eysenck tried to replace all of other talking cures with his own favourite, the action-oriented behaviour therapy (Eysenck, 1952). Almost 50 years later, the psychotherapies have grown – at least in breadth – but now face new challenges. The place of the 'talking cure' within the context of care and treatment remains a hotly debated issue.

New developments in psychopharmacology have produced new drugs, which appear to resolve many of the troubling symptoms associated with anxiety, panic and obsessional disorders, as well as depression, manic-depressive psychosis and schizophrenia. This does not mean, however, that psychotherapy – of any kind – is now redundant. There remains a significant proportion of people for whom drugs will either be inappropriate or only a partial success. The value of appropriate psychotherapy either alone, or as an adjunct to other treatments, looks set to continue.

Economic pressures have led to a proliferation of 'brief therapies'. Although more 'depth-oriented' therapies appear to be excluded by our cost-conscious system, in many cases, an 'in-depth' exploration of the patient's problems may ultimately be the most efficient, if not only, way to address them. There is a need to match therapy to people's wishes (wherever possible) and to the nature of the problem (in all cases).

As large psychiatric hospitals disappear, more people – with more serious forms of mental illness – require more intensive support to live in the community and to avoid re-hospitalisation. These developments have led to the creation of an unfortunate distinction between 'seriously ill' and 'worried well' people. Psychotherapy is concerned, first and foremost, with responding to human need – not economic necessity. However, the focus on people with combinations of mental and social problems, such as those with problems of living associated with chronic psychosis, have stimulated a resurgence of interest in extending traditional, and developing alternative, therapeutic methods for this group of people.

The changes in healthcare – at least in affluent Western societies – now places psychotherapy, also, in a changing context. Psychotherapy has often been viewed as an exclusive area of practice, with an exclusive clientele. Increasingly however, healthcare professionals are developing their awareness of how some of the principles of psychotherapy might be integrated within their professional practice. Such awareness can only increase access to the 'mental healing' that has such a universal history, and may encourage growth within these disciplines and their practitioners.

Footnotes

[1] Although this term has fallen into fashionable disuse, I recognise the original definition pertaining to someone who clearly 'suffers' from something requiring professional attention.

[2] This term was first coined by the American psychoanalyst, Harry Stack Sullivan.

[3] Here I am talking only of those who come voluntarily. People who are sent for therapy represent quite a different scenario.

[4] The use of this term was popularised by Carl Rogers in the 1940s.

References

Corsini, R.J. (1981) *Handbook of Innovative Psychotherapies.* New York: Wiley.

Ellis, A. (1962) *Reason and Emotion in Psychotherapy.* New York: Lyle and Stuart.

Eysenck, H.J. (1952) The effects of psychotherapy: An evaluation. *Journal of Consulting Psychology; 16,* 319-324.

Frank, J.D. (1974) Psychotherapy: The restoration of morale. *American Journal of Psychiatry; 131,* 271-274.

Freud, S. (1952) Postscript to a discussion on lay analysis. In S Freud *Collected Papers,* Vol 5. London: Hogarth Press; pp 205-214.

Herink, R. (ed) (1980) *The Psychotherapy Handbook.* New York: The New American Library.

Newell, R. and Dryden, W. (1991) Clinical problems: An introduction to the cognitive-behavioural approach. In W Dryden and R Rentoul (Eds) *Adult Clinical Problems: A cognitive behavioural approach.* London: Routledge.

Rogers, C.R. (1942) *Counselling and Psychotherapy: Newer concepts in practice.* Boston: Houghton and Mifflin.

Rogers, C. (1961) The characteristics of a helping relationship. In M.I. Stein (Ed) *Contemporary Psychotherapies.* New York: Free Press.

Strupp, H.H. (1972) On the technology of psychotherapy. *Archives of General Psychiatry; 26,* 270-278.

Sullivan, H.S. (1953) The Interpersonal Theory of Psychiatry. New York: Norton.

Wolberg, L. (1995) *The Technique of Psychotherapy* (4th Edition). London: Jason Aronson Inc.

2. Healing the soul: the psychoanalytic psychotherapies

DOCTORING THE SOUL

The origins of modern psychotherapy probably lie in Ancient Greece, with Heraclitus of Ephesus, who developed the concept of the "unity of opposites", more than 2,500 years ago (Chessick, 1987). That ancient idea of the "necessary tension between opposing forces vital to harmonious functioning" was clearly the basis for modern psychodynamics (Wheelwright, 1968). Ever since, philosophers in all cultures have been reflecting on the effects people have on one another, and how we might develop a method to improve society or achieve happiness. Although the modern psychotherapies can be counted, literally, in their hundreds (Herink, 1980), all share those age-old ambitions.

A careful appraisal of mental health practice, however, suggests that the most commonly used therapeutic approach involves an amalgam of psychoanalytic, psychodynamic and interpersonal theories (Schroeder and Benfer, 1990). These theories have had a major impact on the thinking and practice of all disciplines involved in mental healthcare and treatment. Often, however, we are unaware of the extent to which we use the concepts derived from psychodynamic theories to explain both our own actions and experiences, and those of others.

Modern psychotherapy began with Freud, whose psychoanalytic method sought to bring to light the unconscious meaning of the person's talk, action and associated mental images (Ellenberger, 1970). Although few people now receive classical psychoanalytic therapy – which comprises several sessions a week over many years – Freud influenced the development of many methods of therapy and counselling. His belief that we have secret wishes that are held back through the processes of repression and resistance are now part of our vernacular. In keeping with the spirit of his age, Freud developed a dynamic model of the human psyche to explain how personality developed and psychopathology operated. The 'id' is that part of our personality structure that contains our primitive instincts and impulsiveness. The id is held in check – or redirected – by the 'ego', or rational and adaptive part of our personality. The superego – or conscience – expresses the values and rules of our society or culture. Freud's ideas were controversial, not least because they were focused on the role of sexuality, as an invisible, primitive force, in the expression of the whole gamut of human behaviour. Although subsequent theorists, from various schools of psychology, challenged Freud's belief that sexuality lay at the core of human development, few denied the existence of the mental structure, that Freud and his followers attempted to explicate, label and study. Today, many therapists, from a wide range of theoretical persuasions, still accept the notion of the unconscious, and continue to attempt to address the ego defence mechanisms, first labelled by Freud.

Freud's original theory was developed around neurotic symptoms. He believed that everyone was neurotic to some extent, these emotional and behavioural patterns representing the burden of childhood carried over into adult life. Many symptoms were viewed as symbolic: a person who compulsively washed his hands was perhaps trying to rid himself of something from his past that was labelled "unclean" during a critical stage of development. Freud's original theory was extended later by the definition of 12 ego defence mechanisms (Bellak, 1973), each of which has the potential to foster general adaption (ego strength) or maladaption (ego weakness).

A wide range of theorists has influenced the shape and application of Freud's original idea of the unconscious, contributing in turn to the development of different 'schools' of psychotherapy.

▷ Erik Erikson (1959) expanded Freud's developmental focus to cover the whole life cycle: he identified eight life-stages, and saw the problems people experienced in their life as a function of failure to complete the developmental tasks involved in progressing through these life stages.

▶ Anna Freud (1972), Freud's daughter, developed further the concept of defence mechanisms, and focused specifically on children.

▶ Melanie Klein (1932) also worked with children, developing specific psychoanalytic techniques involving play.

▶ Karen Horney (1939) investigated the relationship between behaviour and cultural and interpersonal processes.

▶ Frieda Fromm-Reichmann (1950) was one of the first to explore the application of psychoanalytic method with people in psychotic states.

▶ Karl Menninger (1968) worked specifically on the idea of dynamic equilibrium, expanding the concept of coping as a facet of mental functioning.

▶ Donald Winnicott (1966) worked closely with mothers and children, and developed the radical idea that the therapist's relationship to the patient should be modelled on "an ordinary and devoted mother's holding care of her infant" (Kahn and Winnicott, 1971).

▶ More recently, Otto Kernberg – among others – developed the concept of 'splitting'– where the patient may separate himself (and the nurse) into polar opposites of good and bad (Kernberg, 1975).

Although only now beginning to be re-evaluated, the influence of Harry Stack Sullivan (1953) was considerable, especially his development of an *interpersonal* model.

Until Sullivan, the focus of psychoanalysis had been on the *intrapsychic* world of the patient: what was happening in the internal world of the patient's experience. Sullivan shifted the focus to address the person's social and interpersonal experience – the relation between 'self' and 'others'. Although Sullivan developed his own theory and terminology, the link with Freud remained. For example, whereas Freud talked of the 'ego', Sullivan identified the role of the 'self-system', which was essentially the same invisible core of the person.

Sullivan also believed that early experience influenced mental health in later life. If a child is told repeatedly that he is not to be trusted, he will develop a negative self–system characterised by untrustworthiness. Notably, Sullivan believed that people would only find in others what already existed within the self-system. Therefore, a person who sees himself as untrustworthy, will view others similarly.

In their common interest in people in psychotic states, Sullivan was close to Frieda Fromm-Reichmann (1950), who saw psychoanalytic therapy as being offered in a "spirit of collaboration". In so doing, they began the development of empathy as we understand it today. Sullivan and Fromm-Reichmann's work with people in psychotic states was highly influential in shaping the theory of interpersonal relations in nursing developed by Hildegard Peplau (1952). Peplau followed up Sullivan's interest in the satisfaction and security 'drives'. She defined health as a "forward movement of personality and other ongoing human processes in the direction of creative, constructive, productive, personal and community living."

Although Peplau's original theory was developed for nursing, it is relevant to any therapeutic context. Sullivan had defined the therapist as a *participant observer* who was actively involved with the patient, rather than 'sitting back', as had been the practice within traditional Freudian analysis. The role of the therapist was to engage actively with the patient, establishing trust and, as noted earlier, developing empathy. Sullivan emphasised the importance of 'relating' directly to the patient, validating his experience, helping him appreciate that his perceptions and problems are not all that different from others. Although these approaches are now largely taken for granted as part of the therapeutic or (especially) counselling approach, they derive from Sullivan's and Peplau's ground-breaking work in the 1940s and 1950s.

Sullivan believed that the therapist and the patient were more like one another than different. It is noteworthy that his assertion "everyone is much more simply human than otherwise" was made in the context of working with people in acute psychosis (Sullivan, 1953). Indeed, many of the principles of 'interpersonal therapy' now represent the basis of almost all the therapeutic approaches described in this book:

▶ The therapist tries to create an atmosphere of uncritical acceptance that will encourage the patient to unburden himself;

▶ The therapist shows evidence of his own beliefs, thoughts, feelings and values, which represent his/her 'real nature';

▶ The patient is encouraged to participate to the best of his ability, sharing his thoughts, feelings and problems with the therapist.

The relationship that develops is intended to serve as a model for human relationships outside of therapy. As the patient grows within therapy, these gains may gradually be extended to life experiences beyond the therapeutic setting.

CONTEMPORARY PRACTICE

Traditional psychoanalysis emphasised the use of free association as the central method of exchange between patient and analyst. Contemporary practice has broadened to include more directive action on the part of the therapist and include the following:

▶ The first task is to establish a therapeutic alliance "with the part of the patient's ego that seeks relief from discomfort and is reasonable enough to reason that the analyst's contributions can produce healing" (Lueger and Sheikh, 1989).

▶ At any point in the therapy, resistance may be manifest, through lateness, missed appointments or even dramatic recovery or an expressed wish to terminate therapy. The patient is encouraged to recognise that resistance is an inescapable fact of being human and, in so doing, affects a temporary neurosis, which in time is therapeutic.

▶ The patient begins to experience particular feelings for the therapist (transference), that are often a displacement of feelings experienced in relation to significant others in the patient's life: family, partners, authority figures etc. The feelings experienced can vary from fear of reproach, affection, a sense of kinship or companionship, to anger at being made to feel responsible or accountable for her/his own life. The therapist encourages the patient to recognise that the transference is not produced by the therapy, but is simply activated by the therapeutic relationship.

▶ The therapist uses analytic confrontation to focus the patient's awareness on specific experiences: "you seem to feel angry towards me". Closely linked to this is the use of interpretation, when the therapist tries to make conscious some of the unconscious meanings associated with specific events, and how – developmentally – they may have come about.

▶ Any insights gained at this stage are incorporated in the process of working through, or continual review of the events of the session, to gain new perspectives for both patient and therapist.

▶ Finally, the countertransference that exists between patient and therapist has a major influence on the process of therapy. Various factors influence how the therapist relates to the patient. These stem from conflicts within the therapist – such as a need to be valued, accepted or liked, or a need to strive for power, status or wealth. Unresolved developmental experiences can be resurrected in the therapeutic relationship – especially sibling rivalry, or envy. Signs of countertransference include the following:

▶ An unreasonable dislike for the patient;

▶ Having little feeling for the patient;

▶ Liking the patient excessively;

▶ Dreading the next session with the patient;

▶ Feeling vulnerable to the patient's criticism (Cohen, 1952).

PSYCHODYNAMIC PSYCHOTHERAPY AND NURSING

Peplau (1952) developed several discrete roles for nurses that helped the patient to achieve the goals of therapy: achieving satisfaction and personal growth. These roles included:

▶ Stranger – the nature of the initial relationship;

▶ Resource – providing the patient with information or other supports;

▶ Teacher – helping the patient learn how to benefit from his experience within the healthcare system;

▶ Leader – helping the patient follow democratically determined healthcare routines;

▶ Surrogate – fulfilling roles that represent previous relationships (the transference relationship);

▶ Counsellor – helping the patient to accommodate specific feelings associated with problems of living within his whole life experience.

Even in its simplest form, psychodynamic nursing involves a special kind of confidential relationship aimed at alleviating symptoms and distress through the exploration of the patient's interpersonal life (Lego, 1984):

▶ In the introductory phase, therapist and client assess the 'boundaries' of the relationship. The nurse develops an appreciation of the patient's problems (as well as assets) and characteristic ways of dealing with them; and the patient discovers the nurse's ability to hear and understand.

▶ Once open communication is established, the formal working phase begins. The patient may bring up any issue of personal concern. This may be a current event; some memory, dream or fantasy; or thoughts and feelings about the therapist. These serve as openings into the patient's unconscious. Through talking, the patient becomes sensitive to feelings, conflicts, desires or wishes that previously were beyond awareness. Gradually, the nurse helps the patient develop an appreciation of how these experiences might fit a general pattern in her/his life.

▶ The final stage is termination, which may involve a reawakening of memories of past painful separation. Where the patient wishes to discontinue, this might involve resistance. In either case, these issues need to be addressed.

The nurse evaluates progress constantly, fully aware that changes do not always mean improvement or deterioration. When the person realises – to their satisfaction – that their distress is finally being heard, a 'honeymoon' stage emerges. When long-buried emotions are brought to the surface, the patient may show anger towards the nurse (aggressive stage) and may soon begin to feel more basic insecurities as she/he gives up long-used defences (regressive stage). The nurse expects an adaptive stage to materialise, where new ways of responding indicate the beginnings of resolution of problems (Lego, 1984).

The range of applications of psychodynamic principles is wide indeed: from milieu therapy, where the various needs of different patients are accommodated within a necessarily changing environment (Sills, 1976), through group (Lego, 1993), individual, and family therapy for different clinical groups (Altschul, 1978; Fabricius, 1994; Evans, 1997).

The use of psychodynamic principles – especially for meeting the needs of people with serious forms of mental illness – continues to develop (Winship, 1995 b; Lego, 1996). As mental health nursing begins again to review the importance of the nurse-patient relationship, it may be time to re-examine the contribution made by some of the pioneers of psychodynamic nursing (Travelbee, 1971). In particular, mental health nurses might reconsider the implications of the concept of the 'therapeutic use of self' – a term that risks becoming a nursing cliché. In Joyce Travelbee's original words, this meant:

> "the ability to use one's personality consciously and in full awareness in an attempt to establish relatedness and... requires self-insight, self-understanding, an understanding of the dynamics of human behaviour, ability to interpret one's own behaviour as well as of others... (the therapeutic use of self) implies that the nurse possesses *a profound understanding of the human condition*". (Travelbee, 1971, emphasis added).

The original theoretical work of Freud has been subjected to considerable criticism, especially of late (Masson, 1984). The distinguished psychiatrist Anthony Clare has recently dismissed Freud's early theories as a "farrago of fiction, fantasy and incompetence" based on "case histories [which] were, for the most part, romantic fiction, not clinical fact" (Clare, 1997). These criticisms, even if justified, should not detract from the more recent 'facts', generated by many who followed Freud, including nurses and other mental health disciplines. There appears to be a solid and developing body of evidence that describes the processes by which personalities develop, or are damaged, as a function of human relationships. Although it is possible to help people through difficult stages in their lives, often people feel haunted by their past, and troubled by something that lies (invisibly) beneath their outward exterior. For such people, learning how to confront or cope with life problems may, ultimately, be unsatisfying. For such people, there may be a need to dive deeper into the human psyche.

Nurses and other healthcare professionals who use psychodynamic and psychoanalytic principles in their work may be engaged in the kind of search that the American nurse Travelbee saw as the ideal of psychiatric nursing. Such searching (when necessary) helps patients "find meaning in their experiences (of health and illness)" (Travelbee, 1966). Such meanings are, necessarily, complex. Nurses who recognise the importance of the search for such meanings, and the complex processes involved – like Peplau in the US 50 years ago (O'Toole and Welt, 1989), and Winship in the UK today (Winship, 1995 a) – appreciate that the relationship between nursing and psychoanalysis can be an uneasy alliance. In many disciplines, therapists are encouraged to act 'as if' the abstract processes of the transference and countertransference are no more than figments of the psychoanalyst's imagination. However, as Main illustrated 40 years ago, where nurses tried (unconsciously) to be what their patients projected on to them (Main, 1957), this often led to a sense of emotional draining, or 'burn out'. We need to consider carefully how we answer the question "how might a psychoanalytic approach help address patient's problems?" Given the demands that providing therapeutic care involves, we need also to ask, "how might a psychoanalytic approach help all health and social care staff deal with the closeness of their relationship to people in need of such care and treatment?"

References

Altschul, A. (1978). A systems approach to the nursing process. *Journal of Advanced Nursing; 3*, 333-340

Bellak, L., Hurvich M. and Gediman H.K. (1973) *Ego-Functions in Schizophrenics, Neurotics and Normals: A Systematic study of conceptual, diagnostic and therapeutic aspects.* New York: John Wiley.

Chessick, R. D. (1987) *Great Ideas in Psychotherapy.* London: Jason Aronson Inc pp 27

Clare, A. (1997) That sinking feeling: Review of 'Dr Freud: a life' by Paul Ferris. *The Sunday Times Books,* 16th Nov 1997, pp 10.

Cohen, M.B. (1952) Countertransference and anxiety. *Psychiatry; 15,* 231–243.

Ellenberger, H.F. (1970) *The Discovery of the Unconscious: The history and evolution of dynamic psychiatry.* New York: Basic Books.

Erikson, E. (1959) *Identity and the Life Cycle.* New York: International Universities Press.

Evans, M. (1997) Using a psychoanalytic model to approach acts of self harm. *Nursing Times; 90* (42), 38–40.

Fabricius, J. (1994) Psychodynamic perspectives. In H. Wright and M. Giddey (Eds) *Mental Health Nursing.* London: Chapman and Hall.

Freud, A. (1972) *The Writings of Anna Freud,* 7 vols. New York: International Universities Press.

Fromm-Reichmann, F. (1950) *Principles of the Intensive Psychotherapy.* Chicago: University of Chicago Press.

Herink, R. (1980) *The Psychotherapy Handbook.* New York: The New American Library.

Horney, K. (1939) *New Ways in Psychoanalysis.* New York: W.W. Norton.

Kahn, M. and Winnicott, D.W. (1971) *International Journal of Psychoanalysis;* *52*, 225–226.

Kernberg, O. (1975) *Borderline Conditions and Pathological Narcissism.* New York: Aronson .

Klein, M. (1932) *The Psychoanalysis of Children.* London: Hogarth Press.

Lego, S. (1984) Psychoanalytically oriented individual and group therapy with adults. In D.L. Critchely and J.T. Maurin (Eds) *The Clinical Nurse Specialist in Psychiatric Mental Health Nursing: Theory, research and practice.* New York: John Wiley and Sons.

Lego, S. (1993) The parallel process of resistance by clients and therapist to starting groups: A guide for nurses. *Archives of Psychiatric Nursing; 7* (5), 300–307.

Lego, S. (1996) Psychodynamic individual psychotherapy. In S Lego (Ed) *Psychiatric Nursing: A comprehensive reference,* 2nd edition. New York: Lippincott.

Lueger, R.J. and Sheikh, A.A. (1989) The four forces of psychotherapy. In A.A. Sheikh and K.S. Sheikh (Eds) *Healing East and West: Ancient wisdom and modern psychology.* New York: John Wiley.

Main, T.I. (1957) *British Journal of Medical Psychology; 30,* 129–145.

Masson, J.M. (1984) *Freud: The assault on truth.* London: Faber.

Menninger, K. (1968) *The Total Balance.* New York: Viking Press.

O'Toole, A. and Welt S.R. (Eds) (1989) *Interpersonal Theory in Nursing Practice: Selected works of Hildegard E Peplau.* London: Macmillan.

Peplau, H.E. (1952) *Interpersonal Relations in Nursing.* New York: Putnam.

Schroeder, P. and Benfer, B. (1990) The eclectic approach: principles and application. In W. Reynolds and D. Cormack (Eds) *Psychiatric and Mental Health Nursing: Theory and practice.* London: Chapman and Hall.

Sills, G. (1976) Use of milieu therapy in psychiatric nursing – 1946–74: A report on the state of the art. *American Journal of Nursing; 76,* 23-25.

Sullivan, H.S. (1953) *The Interpersonal Theory of Psychiatry.* New York: Norton.

Travelbee, J. (1966) *Interpersonal Aspects of Nursing.* Philadelphia; FA Davis.

Travelbee, J. (1971) *Interpersonal Aspects of Nursing,* 2nd edition. Philadelphia.

Wheelwright, P. (1968) *Heraclitus.* New York: Atheneum Press.

Winnicott, D.W. (1966) *The Maturational Processes and the Facilitating Environment.* New York: International Universities Press.

Winship, G. (1995a) Nursing and psychoanalysis – uneasy alliances? *Psychoanalytic Psychotherapy; 9* (3), 289-299.

Winship, G. (1995b) The unconscious impact of caring for acutely disturbed patients: A perspective for supervision. *Journal of Psychiatric and Mental Health Nursing; 2*(4), 227-232.

Case study 1

PSYCHOANALYTIC SHORT-TERM THERAPY WITH A DIABETIC PATIENT

Martin Teising

'Representations' are modules of the largely unconscious inner reality, which form their own, mainly unconscious, representational world. They are formed as much by instinctual impulses as by processes of perception, thought and defence. Their cores are structured at an early infantile stage and keep undergoing a life-long transformation, especially the representations of one's own body. Experiences of illness can become intertwined with pre-existing experiences, forming a representation of illness *and* therapy, as in this case.

When I first met John, a 46-year-old type-I diabetic, he was studying information on complications of diabetes posted in the hallway. I had an impression that he was concentrating hard on this. As I moved to carry another chair into the room, John jumped to my aid, taking the chair for me. There was an upholstered chair and an unpadded one, and I offered him the more comfortable. However, he quickly but politely chose the unpadded chair. He was submitting himself, but also deciding where I would sit.

As we faced each other, I noted the ascetic features: his fair full beard, gold-rimmed glasses and sporty clothes. He smiled, a little rigidly, with an expression of tense, special anticipation. "Six years ago, the thing with the diabetes took a bad turn," he said. It started with a sporting accident requiring surgery and a six-month stay in bed, and for a time, his leg was in danger of amputation. During that time, his diabetes decompensated, with renal disease and high blood pressure emerging. He almost lost his eyesight and needed to use a reading device. As he talked, I remembered that the hallway posters described retinal complications in diabetes. I was alarmed and felt guilty, wondering if John was burdened with this confrontation. As he recounted additional dangerous physical damage, I felt very sorry for him, but found I could say nothing. I felt hopeless and realised that any consoling words would be designed to comfort me. I thought I saw tears in his eyes, but realised I only read them into his eyes because I was so deeply touched.

I learned how active John had been until the accident. Although he had been diabetic since he was 17, he became a skiing instructor, mountain guide and soccer player, ignoring the first signs of diabetic complications. However, after the injury, his fitness collapsed. His body was no longer under control.

I then understood how he had not wanted to appear an invalid, carrying the chair for himself, choosing the uncomfortable chair to demonstrate his fitness. I began to feel his helplessness, which had begun six years previously, the point at which he had begun to talk. John had used his physical prowess to ward off the threat imposed by the illness. The combative moment, which dominated his defence, was replicated in our brief relationship. He had fought with me to avoid feeling intimidated. He experienced meeting me in the same way as the challenge of the illness.

He had to control the situation because, he said, "The diabetes is in me and eats at each body cell." He sensed it as an orally sadistic, destructive enemy to be avoided or removed. By placing his helplessness within me through projective identification, he could keep things under control. My feeling of helplessness resulted from fear that I had harmed him by exposing him to the posters, for which I wasn't even responsible. This helpless feeling was an introjection of the patient's projection. John projected his aggressive impulses on to me as well as on to his diabetes. His aggression towards the diabetes was a defence against helplessness at the hands of the disease as well as me. He experienced the aggressive impulses not only as a part of his own self, but as a characteristic of his diabetes, which dominated his insides and, thus, remained part of his own ego.

The decisive qualities of his concept of the illness were experienced 'physically' by me during the interview. I was especially impressed in this first conversation by his words that his diabetes was "in me and eats at each body cell". This was physiologically literal but also a metaphor. Connecting this metaphorical image with the scene with the chairs, I said that I had the impression that he felt very threatened by this illness. It had forced its way into him, and he was very much on his guard to control the situation, which he had done successfully for a long time. John was surprised, but considered this and agreed. His emotional state thus became the subject of our conversation, and we agreed to meet weekly for short-term, psychoanalytic therapy.

In these few sessions, he became aware of how much his pre-existing relationships and body representations had determined his experience of both his illness and the therapy. He remembered how his mother had told him that his father had been a diabetic. John did not know his father because his mother had never lived with him, characterising him as a "freeloader" who was only interested in "sucking" her financially. John became aware that he had transferred this 'sucking' quality to his diabetic illness, which he thought came from his father.

He had also learned from his mother to be polite and courteous towards strangers, but at the same time, sceptical. She said he must not "let them get the better of me", and he always had to keep himself and situations under control. It was impressive to observe (in the (counter-) transference situation) how his representations of relationships were intertwined with representations of his diabetes and the therapeutic relationship.

In the nurse-patient relationship, each patient brings into the transference other relationship experiences and, when in crisis, regresses to very early-life experiences, as early internal relationship patterns and experiences become dominant. The basic feeling of physical or psychic coherence is lost, and anxiety occurs. In such circumstances, nurses have to ensure the patient's existential cohesion, although this may be unbeknown to the patient.

Patients often handle their illness with the help of splitting and projecting defence mechanisms. Some patients seek refuge from their 'bad objects' with nurses; others feel at the mercy of the 'bad object nurse' and fight for their self-determination. The latter was very much the case with John.

A psychodynamic understanding of the illness, based on the model of the bad internal object, which needs to be fought, corresponds with the prevailing model of medicine and nursing, where the person's functioning is interfered with by an external agent that 'breaks through' the body's defences. This traumatic agent can take many forms, and be of a physical, chemical, biological or mental nature.

Although this conception can be very successful in combating symptoms, the combat is often unconsciously not desired. The patient may be quite ambivalent about the illness, viewing it as a naughty child, which he/she wishes rid of, but would miss all the same if was gone.

Such a 'paranoid-schizoid' understanding of illness is often accompanied by the idealisation of the nurse, upon which the patient projects fantasies of omnipotence. When the patient is disappointed, as inevitably happens, the patient's idealisation of the nurse can turn to devaluation.

The patient, unconsciously, does not always view the nurse as a helpful object, but as an object connected with the illness. After all, the nurse only emerged at the same time as the disease and, unconsciously, remains linked to it, even though she considers herself the patient's ally in the joint 'fight against the illness'.

Feelings of threat can manifest themselves in the nurse having been split off by the patient for his own protection, and deposited in the nurse like in a container. This happened in the reported case. In addition to these projections, nurses have their own feelings and emotions. If the feelings involved become conscious and can even be discussed, both the patient and the nurse can fall back on each other, developing more favourable mechanisms to cope with the illness.

In our therapy, some of these intertwinements could be undone by becoming more open to experience. Thus, John's experience also became understandable, e.g., that John's illness was formed by unconscious guilt feelings of having driven away his father. These guilt feelings, which also fed on his fantasy of him being a diabetic sucking and feeding on each cell, were the source of his deportment. With increasing discernment of the unconscious fears, which the patient attributed to his illness because of his individual conflict situation, he was able to find a more rational way of coping with his illness. The metabolic regulation has now been as stable for four years as it had not been for the previous six years.

References

Argelander, H. (1970) *Das Erstinterview in der Psychotherapie*. Darmstadt: Wissenschaftliche Buchgesellschaft.

Ogden, T.H. (1989) On the concept of an autistic-contiguous position. *International Journal of Psycho-Analysis; 70*, 127–140.

Sandler, J., Rosenblatt, B. (1962) The concept of the representational world. *Psychoanalytical Study of the Child; 17*, 128–145.

Case study 2

PSYCHODYNAMIC GROUPWORK WITH PARENTS

Sue Croom

Parenting can often be a difficult experience. For parents of children with developmental or psychological problems, the experience can be deeply troubling. Parents of children experiencing the group described here aimed to develop support among a group of parents, promoting knowledge and skills in understanding and managing their children who were aged four to 10 years. Although the group was open to both mothers and fathers, it consisted entirely of mothers, most of whom were single parents.

At the outset, the mothers admitted to being uncertain about the group, saying things like "I've never done anything like this before". They looked visibly nervous and tended to listen and observe more than interact. The non-verbal cues picked up by the two nurse facilitators indicated that the parents were highly fragile, exhausted, worn down and unsure of themselves. This elicited feelings of wanting to nurture the parents. Responding to this affective data and to cognitive knowledge regarding the development of a psychotherapeutic group, the nurses attempted to promote a sense of trust and acceptance in the group. Verbal reassurances about the aims of the group were given with an emphasis on partnering the mothers, engaging in reciprocal learning. However, what seemed to be more powerful in developing the sense of trust was responding to the parents' cues of needing to be nurtured – e.g., offering drinks and serving them, or offering a coat when one mother was cold. This elicited a response of "We get well looked after here, don't we?" The power of this nurturance was illustrated when one nurse acknowledged that a mother looked tired. It transpired that she had suffered from toothache all weekend, and the nurse offered some analgesia to relieve the pain. In about ten minutes, the mother looked and said she felt much better and began interacting in a positive way. The soothing of what had been considerable physical pain was arguably a symbolic sign of the soothing of the deeper psychic pain, that this mother felt and later was able to discuss openly.

The nurses reflected on the emotional barometer prompted by the transference from the group members to the nurses. We (the nurses) did not wish to encourage a sense of dependence. We acknowledged, however, that nurture was the first step on the journey in a dynamic group process, which could gradually support the parents in developing positive identities as parents and individuals. In turn, this could promote their confidence in problem solving, which could allow them to develop an enriched relationship with their children. The mothers appeared to have lost all sense of themselves, and defined themselves totally in terms of being caregivers to their children. They seemed genuinely surprised by being listened to, and greatly appreciated it. Their sense of trust gradually grew as they discovered that they would not be judged, even when they disclosed incidents that they perceived as examples of their failures as mothers (and therefore of themselves). Not only were they still valued by group members, but they were actually helped to reflect on how caring they actually were as individuals. One mother described how she had lost her temper with her child and had shouted at him, saying how totally fed up she was with him. She was distressed by her hostility towards him. The group members empathised with her feelings and identified with her distress. On further exploration, the mother identified that soon after this incident, her little boy had been upset by another child. He had turned to her for comfort and she had responded with great sensitivity. When we put it to her that her true caring as a mother was expressed through this response, both she and the rest of the mothers agreed that this made sense, but said that they often found it difficult to forgive themselves in such circumstances. Sometimes they felt like loving caring mothers, but seemed too ready to condemn themselves as 'bad mothers'. They were not always able to challenge these feelings with their very caring attitudes. This often produced intense guilt feelings, which were extremely difficult to deal with. Acknowledging this and their tendency to perceive themselves as 'all bad' or 'all good' mothers seemed to be critical in resolving the 'splitting' process, and to integrating their identity as mothers who were not perfect, but who were very loving and caring.

Raising their awareness of the importance of their positive sense of identity provided the foundation for being able to integrate the 'good' and 'bad' aspects of their children (all of whom were difficult to manage). Ultimately, this helped them to appreciate the importance of communicating a sense of acceptance, value and love for their children, although not necessarily condoning their behaviour. Initially in the group, there were many negative attributions of their children's behaviour: "they just do it to wind me up…" "they seem to enjoy upsetting everybody". By listening to and acknowledging the distress, which could arise when coping with difficult children, as well as dealing with housing problems, schools, neighbours and money worries, the mothers developed an awareness of the very high levels of daily arousal they experienced. This promoted an understanding of how this arousal could often be projected onto their partners, children or school, and could create a vicious circle. By discussing these stresses in the group, they could alleviate the stress, which helped them cope with such difficulties. This helped the mothers to be more emotionally available to their children, and also to empathise with the distress of children who temperamentally were impulsive, unable to tolerate the arousal created by everyday frustrations, and therefore often displayed their anxiety in the form of aggressive or oppositional behaviour. This gradually allowed the mothers to reframe their attributions of their children from 'naughty/bad' children, to children who needed particular types of understanding and management.

The mothers gradually admitted to feeling "more in tune" or "more connected" to their children. As this happened, things started to improve in many other ways. We were attempting to tune into the verbal and non-verbal communication of the mothers, and at the same time encouraging them to be able to predict a positive and supportive response from us. This mutual process appeared to help foster a sense of trust and attachment in the group similar to the mother-infant attachment process. Helping the mothers to feel valued enabled them to value and empathise with others. The mothers' own range of life stresses had diminished their sense of value. This had left them with reduced emotional resources to be able to tune into children who were temperamentally difficult to manage and unpredictable, and therefore, ironically, in need of an even greater sensitivity. Once the mothers felt that their own sense of self-worth was restored and their own nurturing needs were met, they were able to become more emotionally available to their children.

Valuing themselves was poignantly revealed when mothers said things like:

▶ "I bought an ice cream. It was just something for me and it felt good";

▶ "I usually spent all my money on them but I bought a pair of socks – 99p – but they were for me and I felt OK about it".

A very painful issue, which emerged as the sense of trust in the group grew, was the sense of ambivalence the mothers sometimes felt towards their children. One mother admitted:

▶ "I've felt terrible this week. I've found myself thinking what life would be like if I hadn't had (child's name), if I only had the girls… but then I can't bear this thought… I feel so guilty that I've got to do something to distract myself. I'll get up and I'll do a jigsaw with him just to take my mind off it and prove I love him."

The perception that at times they may not love their child was unbearable to the mothers, and they were unable to tolerate these feelings. In fact, the group was the first place they had actually openly admitted it, because the accompanying guilt was overwhelming. Bringing into awareness and acknowledging these feelings helped the mothers resolve these previously repressed feelings. We were able to discuss the 'normality' of ambivalence in close relationships, and we talked about research that had shown that once parents acknowledged this ambivalence – the love/hate component – they were galvanised in the way the mother who told her story was. However, if parents did not acknowledge such feelings, all kinds of problems might emerge. The mother might project her anxiety and anger over having these feelings on to her child, thus fuelling relationship difficulties.

As nurses, we felt and acknowledged a growing sense of closeness to the mothers and wished to use this close relationship in a developmentally therapeutic way. We wanted to facilitate a greater sense of autonomy and competence in the mothers. This process mirrors Erikson's psychodynamic developmental process, in which the caregiver promotes a sense of autonomy in individuals, gradually supporting them to cope with stressful situations. The parents gradually began to use the group to develop their sense of confidence and competence in problem solving:

▶ "I feel as if I can cope during the week because I know that whatever happens, I'm going to be able to get it off my chest at the group."

▶ "Just talking about things, getting them off your chest can help."

▶ "Listening to how other people have coped or just being able to understand what is going on can make you feel better."

As the sessions progressed, the feelings of the facilitators registered significant changes. We felt much less the 'leaders and nurturers' of the group, but active participants in a reciprocal learning process. This was illustrated by an incident in which one of the mothers came in extremely tearful and upset because of problems with her neighbours. This time, the other mothers initiated the care, offered a cuddle and talked the situation through, offering suggestions on how to cope. The following week, the same mother came in with make-up and a new outfit, looking much happier, and reported that she had been assertive and coped with the situation so well that she had actually been out with the 'troublesome' neighbours for a social evening. One of the other mothers said very supportively "I told you it wasn't you that was the problem, hinnie". Dealing competently with neighbours was also significant in reducing the stress with her son, who the mother saw as the 'source' of the argument with the neighbours. She and the other mothers began to acknowledge that on difficult estates, on which they all lived, they and their children frequently became scapegoats as other people on the estate projected their stresses on to them. Developing awareness of this changed their attitude to their children. One mother said:

> "I used to react every time someone came to the door complaining about (child's name), but now I don't. I realise it's not always his fault, and I stop and think about it more."

This exploration also helped us as nurses to develop an acute awareness of the myriad external stresses faced by parents of children who are perceived as difficult to manage.

As the group came to an end, the mothers no longer felt the need for facilitation. Indeed, we recognised that the mothers had grown into a well functioning group of highly competent and skilled individuals. However, we could evaluate how much we had each learned from one another. The mothers decided, however, that they wished to retain contact with each other on a less formal basis. The evaluation of the mothers, in terms of increased self-esteem and feelings of being in tune with their children, provided an important measure of the effectiveness of the group. Where nurses are working on a microanalytical level, with verbal and non-verbal cues, in promoting growth and change, it is possible to experience a great sense of exhilaration, respect, personal growth and privilege in sharing experiences with remarkable women. As facilitators, we felt that these experiences were also vital measures of an effective mutual journey between nurses and their clients.

3. Fixing the function: the behavioural psychotherapies

ROOTS AND BRANCHES

The behavioural therapies are often viewed as a relatively new psychotherapeutic development, less than 50 years old. However, the *practice* of behavioural forms of therapy is much older[5], and the philosophical roots of this approach extend back to Aristotle's belief in the central importance of man's pursuit of pleasure and avoidance of pain (Aristotle, 1941)[6]. The behavioural psychotherapies emerged in the 1950s as a serious challenge to the established power of psychoanalysis, to become the Second Force in psychotherapy. Although often perceived as a singular approach, this school owes its allegiance to a wide range of theories, and has spawned an equally heterogeneous group of methods. As will be illustrated here, the actual practice and human focus of the behavioural psychotherapies does not differ greatly from that of psychoanalysis, its original great rival. Indeed, the main bones of contention between the First and Second Forces lay in disagreements about the philosophy of human nature, what constituted evidence, and especially in the 'meaning' of behaviour (see Lueger and Sheikh, 1996).

These disagreements led behavioural psychotherapists, of course, to try to distinguish themselves from psychoanalytic psychotherapists in their practice. However, as the chart of the development of the behavioural psychotherapies will show, they have returned, almost full-circle, to address, in a similar manner, many of the issues that behavioural theory and philosophy initially rejected.

The origins of behaviour therapy probably lie with the British empirical philosophers Locke and Hume, whose mechanistic phenomenology depicted the 'organism' in relation to an external environment, which was the true source of all action and behaviour (Teichman and Evans, 1995). At the turn of the century, E L Thorndike capitalised on these philosophical premises, developing the first theory of 'associative learning' in his stimulus-response learning (Thorndike, 1970). Although later theorists would shift the actual point at which 'learning' occurs, Thorndike's three basic elements – the antecedent (stimulus) behaviour and consequence (reinforcement) remain key features of behavioural psychotherapy, and are still found in contemporary therapists' 'functional analysis of behaviour'.

Thirty years later, B F Skinner – the most famous behaviourist of all – developed Thorndike's law of effect into operant conditioning (Skinner, 1938). Skinner's main contribution was to elucidate the function of schedules of reinforcement in shaping and subsequently maintaining stable patterns of behaviour. Although he never denied the existence of thinking (which he referred to as "the black box"), he argued that its importance had been overemphasised by all intrapsychic theorists, even suggesting that thoughts were "fictions" developed to account for "poorly defined behaviours" (Skinner, 1953). The behaviourist's dogmatic insistence on studying only observable behaviour was stimulated by Skinner, and despite the many changes to practice down the years, this still emphasised in the goal plans of the behavioural psychotherapist.

Pavlov, a Russian physiologist, was a contemporary of Thorndike who developed a different, but related, conditioning theory. This was based on his discovery that salivation could be induced in dogs by repeated pairing of a bell or a light with exposure to food. Pavlov's *classical conditioning* appeared to explain the genesis of behaviour mediated by the autonomic nervous system. This discovery partnered Skinner's operant conditioning, in appearing to offer a two-handed explanation of the genesis of all human behaviour.

John B Watson, an academic psychologist, championed these conditioning theories in the United States, most infamously in his 'creation' of an experimental phobia in 'little Albert', an 11-month-old boy. Making loud noises whenever Albert touched a white rat led to the child gradually avoiding the animal, and led him to apparently generalise his 'fear' to any white fur, including a Santa Claus mask. Watson thought he had discovered the simplest explanation for the genesis of fears and phobias, if not all neurotic disorders. However, due largely to the fast-growing power of psychoanalysis, it was to take 30 years before these theoretical principles became established as a clinical psychotherapeutic practice.

It is perhaps no accident that these two prongs of *behaviourism* were led and developed by academics who were attracted by the emphasis on scientific rigour and the possibility of verifying the results of their work on humans by empirical means. These developments represented the coming of age of a psychological movement that, years earlier, had turned its back on consciousness in favour of the objective measurement of behaviour (Robinson, 1986). At the close of the century, the influence of Locke's empiricism and the radical behaviourist's focus on observable behaviour have re-materialised in the call for more 'evidence-based healthcare'.

A "SECOND FORCE" IN PSYCHOTHERAPY

Although Skinner was the first to talk of 'behaviour therapy' (see Barker, 1982), the first formal application of learning theory, as a therapy, was made by Joseph Wolpe, in South Africa, at the end of World War II (Wolpe, 1958). Wolpe saw many clinical problems as anxiety-based[7] and went on to describe 14 different "counter-conditioning" techniques to treat them. In his systematic desensitisation technique, the patient was exposed in graded stages to an anxiety-provoking situation. By pairing this exposure with relaxation (a competing response), Wolpe showed how anxiety could be inhibited, calling this process "reciprocal inhibition". Wolpe also demonstrated how specific behaviours within the patient's repertoire, could be developed to inhibit anxiety. In particular, he developed the concept of 'assertion', which was to be popularised 20 years later as a discrete therapy: assertiveness training (Liberman et al, 1975). Wolpe described how the experience of anxiety prevented the patient from expressing opinions. By encouraging a specific form of 'acting out', the therapist helped the person inhibit his anxiety, with each act of 'assertion'(Wolpe et al, 1964).

Later, other theorists would argue that Wolpe's method could also be explained, firstly, by Skinner's operant theory since the person was 'learning' how to face a fear situation, and later by cognitive theory, which indicated that specific 'mediational processes' were responsible for the change. Practitioners dismissed most of these early academic disagreements largely as irrelevancies. However, in the 1970s, following a thorough survey of all human 'conditioning' studies, Brewer (1974) concluded that, although 'conditioning' might occur in animals, there was no good evidence of it in studies of humans. More importantly, given that most of Wolpe's methods were originally done 'in imagination', they were much more complex than mere 'conditioning' and were, in effect, early forms of 'cognitive therapy'[8].

Whereas Wolpe had exploited classical conditioning with anxiety-based problems, Skinner's operant conditioning had been applied first within education, and was introduced into psychiatry only in the early 1960s, in an effort to explain how psychotic behaviour might have been 'conditioned' by the institutional environment (Ayllon and Azrin, 1965). Like J B Watson, 50 years earlier, these young psychologists used operant learning theory to illustrate how specific patterns of behaviour could be shaped in individual patients (of a long-stay hospital ward), through the process of reinforcement. They concluded, quite inappropriately, that this was the simplest possible explanation for 'psychotic behaviour', and could explain all other forms of similar behaviour.

As a therapy, operant conditioning enjoyed a brief, but spectacular, period of success. In time, it was to play a central role in many of the 'human development' therapies, which bridged humanistic and behavioural psychotherapy – such as social skills, assertiveness training (Liberman et al, 1975), and some forms of marital therapy (Azrin and Naster, 1973). Ayllon and Azrin's work was developed most famously in the token economy system. Their research, involving the chronically mentally ill and people with learning disabilities, showed highly effective results (Paul and Lentz, 1977). However, in most clinical settings, these programmes became little more than a means of controlling patients further – a more sophisticated form of institutionalisation. However, 20 years after these seminal studies, other researchers and therapists would use some operant learning principles, in combination with other cognitive theories, to produce a range of new approaches for people in psychosis (Birchwood and Preston, 1991).

THINKING, FEELING AND BEHAVIOUR

Psychoanalytic psychotherapists had argued that the behavioural therapies dealt either with only trivial forms of behaviour or focused on 'symptoms', to the detriment of more deep-seated problems. Such criticisms were focused on behaviour therapists who, in the late 1950s and early 1960s, largely ignored 'thinking', far less considered issues such as personality structure. By the late 1960s, however, Albert Bandura had developed a new learning theory which incorporated 'information processing' – the 'black box' that so irritated Skinner (Bandura, 1969). Bandura's social learning theory emphasised the role of various cognitive processes in the acquisition and maintenance of emotional and functional behaviour. His description of 'modelling' exploded the simplistic models offered by operant and classical conditioning. In particular, Bandura illustrated how a person had to attend to a model and needed to be able to retain what had been witnessed, in order to reproduce later the modelled behaviour. Most important of all, perhaps, the person needed to have the motivation to attempt, later, a copy of the modelled behaviour. Bandura's explication of these four mediational processes rekindled an interest in 'cognition' within behaviour therapy. He also linked the study of the individual with a consideration of the influence of social factors, such as values and norms. Bandura's development of a plausible rationale for learning by imitation also helped establish further the modelling role of the therapist in the therapeutic relationship. His social learning theory became the basis of a range of behavioural group therapies, and much later helped foster the concepts of mutual support and self-help groups. In the mid-1970s, he proposed the concept of self-efficacy (Bandura 1977) as a major determinant of human behaviour. In any situation, people had to consider not only the likelihood that a particular behaviour might be reinforced (outcome expectancy), but also had to consider beliefs about their own capacity to perform the behaviour (self-efficacy beliefs).

Michael Mahoney developed Bandura's emphasis on information processing further, showing how people used complex cognitive processes either to generate behaviours or to attach specific meaning to events (Mahoney, 1974). These 'thoughts' and 'beliefs' in turn influenced their reactions to such events. An anxious airline passenger does not react to the sounds of the plane during take-off, but might label the sounds incorrectly: "we've lost an engine... or a wheel!" Alternatively, the person might anticipate or imagine an outcome that is unlikely or impossible – "If I don't wash my hands, God will punish me". Mahoney's original ideas about the relationship between cognition and behaviour led others to begin to explore what "people were saying to themselves" as they behaved in particular ways. However, Mahoney's cognitive stance also had an immediate application, providing the basis for a range of new 'cognitive-behavioural' techniques, through which people could imagine positive (rather than negative) outcomes, and also rehearse (mentally) their exposure to feared stimuli.

Mahoney's (1974) cognitive theory developed, like Abraham Maslow's before him, from a study of high-achievers – elite athletes. Here, Mahoney discovered that the simple (though complex) act of *imagining* the performance of a specific behaviour – such as throwing a basketball – could improve performance, better than practice itself. Mahoney's work eventually became the basis for contemporary sports psychology. More recently, Mahoney's influence is to be found in a whole range of 'New Age' therapies that employ information processing, such as "creative visualisation" (Shone, 1984).

Arnold Lazarus (1971), a contemporary of Mahoney, developed multimodal therapy, which separated problems into Behaviour, Affect, Sensation, Imagery, Cognition, Interpersonal relations and Drug effects (BASIC-ID). These developments signalled the beginning of the end of the influence of learning theory in behaviour therapy, and a blurring of relations with other approaches, especially the humanistic therapies. Lazarus' work provided a structure upon which to build a more comprehensive form of therapy, and forecast the birth of a new pragmatism, one that acknowledged the complexity of the person who was the patient (Lazarus, 1973).

AN ENGLISH INTERLUDE

All these developments stemmed from North American initiatives. In the UK in the 1950s and 60s, a much narrower school of behaviour therapy had been developed by Hans Eysenck (1959), based on the original conditioning theories. Eysenck's methods relied heavily on the therapist controlling the 'counter-conditioning', or 'teaching' the patient how to "learn the *absurdity* (sic) of his conditioned response" (Eysenck, 1987). Although the techniques appeared effective, Eysenck's extremely sober descriptions of the 'counter-conditioning' process earned behaviour therapists the unfortunate reputation of being cold and heartless manipulators.

Eysenck was also famous for his critique of psychoanalysis in the early 1950s (Eysenck, 1952), arguing that as many as two-thirds of patients, treated in psychoanalysis recovered by "spontaneous remission". Eysenck's academic work on behaviour therapy was developed into a 'Maudsley school', where Isaac Marks pioneered exposure therapy for a whole range of anxiety-mediated disorders. In keeping with Eysenck's original resistance to dealing with anything other than behaviour, Marks maintained, for many years, a similar opposition to the emergence of cognitive therapy (Marks, 1987). The work of Marks and his colleagues (see also Marks et al, 1976), however, was used as the basis for the first training of nurses as autonomous behavioural psychotherapists, and represented a major shift in the power base of psychotherapy in the UK.

THE SECOND COGNITIVE REVOLUTION

By the late 1970s the cognitive revolution had overtaken behaviour therapy in the United States. The psychiatrist Aaron Beck's (1976) *cognitive therapy* was a variant of the Rational Emotive Therapy (RET) developed much earlier by the psychologist Albert Ellis (1962). Both Ellis and Beck had become disenchanted with psychoanalysis. Ellis had actually developed his method as a way of combating his own shyness. His therapy included a highly innovative and plausible theory of how the person's beliefs – about himself and the world – influenced feelings and, indirectly, behaviour. Ellis' model involved a cognitive reformulation of the ABC model first developed by Thorndike, with (A)ctivating events, being mediated by (B)eliefs that, in turn, gave rise to emotional, cognitive and behavioural (C)onsequences. His therapy focused on making powerful challenges to the Irrational Beliefs (IBs) that generated distress in the patient, in an attempt to establish more rational ways of thinking.

Ellis' application of this theory was highly creative and often irreverent. He popularised the idea of patients doing 'homework assignments' and would encourage groups of patients to sing specially written songs, describing their anxieties, woes or fears, to the tune of *Yankee Doodle Dandy!* Ellis described RET as a humanistic therapy. He saw the therapist's task as challenging and confronting the person's beliefs, all the time validating their inherent human value.

Whereas Ellis' RET focused from the outset on the patient's irrational beliefs, Beck's cognitive therapy was, structurally, more complex. Beck's cognitive therapy also emphasised the 'distorted' nature of thinking –

looking for evidence to account (for example) for a particular fear – whereas for Ellis, it was 'irrational'– what would be so 'catastrophic' if this happened anyway?

The therapeutic package Beck developed included various behavioural and cognitive techniques, some aimed at reducing distress, but most being used to facilitate understanding of the content and function of the patient's thinking. Beck believed that the patient made rules for himself that were, ultimately, self-defeating. Two main rule-classes were identified:

- The *pleasure-pain* class: where the patient believes (for example) that "I can never be happy unless I am famous";

- The *safety-danger* class: where the patient believes (for example) that "it is awful if people criticise me".

Beck illustrated a number of discrete ways that the patient might show distorted thinking:

- *Personalisation:* attributing events, incorrectly, to his own actions;

- *Polarised thinking:* seeing life only in 'black and white' – things are either right or wrong;

- *Selective abstraction:* attending to the details of a situation, rather than seeing the whole context;

- *Arbitrary inference:* drawing conclusions (usually negative) that cannot be supported by the facts of the situation;

- *Over-generalisation:* assuming (for example) that a single event can represent the totality of the situation.

Beck favoured a highly structured format to the session, believing that this sense of order would meet the patient's needs. The maximum number of sessions is established at the outset, thereby establishing a time limit for the therapeutic relationship, and the patient is encouraged to comment (critically) on the therapist's performance, thereby enhancing the sense of a 'therapeutic alliance'. As with Ellis, homework assignments are central to Beck's model, and therapist and patient invariably rehearse *why* and *how* the homework task should be tackled.

This *cognitive-behavioural* approach is now used widely as a treatment of choice for a wide range of clinical problems, from anxiety and sexual problems to problems associated with schizophrenia and substance abuse (Dryden and Rentoul, 1991).

Psychologists led the development of the behavioural psychotherapies first and, with growing disenchantment with psychoanalysis, some psychiatrists then began to take a key role. The involvement of nurses was restricted initially to a role as 'technician' for the experimental psychologists working in long-stay hospitals in the 1960s. As noted above, in the 1970s, small numbers of nurses began to practise more autonomously as therapists, initially treating only a limited range of neuroses (Marks et al, 1976), but later working with a broader range of life problems (Barker and Fraser, 1985). The application of behavioural psychotherapies has changed greatly over the past 20 years, with many nurses applying the approach across a range of settings, from work with children and adolescents, to liaison psychiatry. Today's cognitive-behavioural therapies are also more complex than anything that Skinner and Wolpe might have imagined, extending to include links with humanistic and existential therapies (Barker, 1992), the self-help movement (Barker, 1994) and even to a merger with psychoanalysis, in the form of cognitive-analytic therapy (Ryle, 1994). Behavioural psychotherapy has also enjoyed, for 20 years, an important role as an adjunct to the treatment of a range of physical disorders, including asthma, insomnia, obesity, pain, cardiovascular disease and habit disorders such as smoking and overeating (see Lazarus, 1984).

Despite the methodological differences between the various 'cognitive' theorists, contemporary behavioural psychotherapists are united by the following assumptions:

▶ Cognitions exist, that mediate the problems of living experienced by the patient;

▶ Cognitions are not only available to the patient for study, but are amenable to change by the patient;

▶ Cognitions are the primary target for change, if the patient's cognitive, emotional or behavioural problems are to be resolved.

The behavioural psychotherapies are still developing, especially in the area of self-management, although relationships with humanistic therapies were first explored 25 years ago, in Lazarus' multimodal therapy (1973). Perhaps, however, the origins of today's interest in self-management, and the active engagement of the patient in therapy, have been growing for more than 20 years. One key influence was Mahoney's notion of the "personal scientist". (Mahoney, 1974). In Mahoney's view, the therapist was not so much a healer as someone who provided a specific structure, within which the patient could heal himself. Mahoney believed that the patient needed a range of ways of coping with his difficulties, and the therapist helped to develop these through the following seven stages:

1 The patient is encouraged to look at upon therapy as a problem-solving process, viewing his problems as a function of a combination of events, some stemming from his environment, and some coming from 'within' himself. He is encouraged to assume responsibility for solving his problems, using the therapist as a 'technical consultant'[9]. In this first phase, all attention is focused on the patient's expectations.

2 The patient is then given support to define his complaint more specifically – operationalising his 'strengths' and 'weaknesses', working out how he might measure change in these aspects of his life.

3 The patient is then shown how he can study his problem in more detail, through systematic record keeping, exposing the possible 'antecedents' and 'consequences' to specific actions on his part (the functional analysis of behaviour). This self-monitoring also includes the patient's thoughts and feelings associated with specific actions in everyday life.

4 Once the problem has been sufficiently analysed, the patient is helped to address it by use of a range of general coping skills – relaxation, distraction or self-instruction. Here, the therapist's function comes to the fore, offering specific suggestions as to possible courses of action.

5 The patient is now ready to test out his new found skills in a 'live experiment'. Over a period of at least two weeks, the patient is encouraged to monitor 'what happens' when he employs these alternatives to his usual way of functioning.

6 Therapist and patient can now review progress, developing aspects of the programme that appear to be 'working' for the patient, and considering alternatives where success has been more limited or short-lived.

7 Finally, the therapy sessions are spaced out to allow the patient to take greater charge of the process of change, leading to termination.

Mahoney's belief that the patients could become their own 'personal scientists' is writ large in the work of contemporary behavioural psychotherapists, who try to avoid the problems of dependency, found in some other therapies, by fostering a therapeutic alliance as early as possible. Thus, the authoritative status of the therapist is given much less emphasis, as the therapist encourages the patient to study himself, his own actions and reactions, and the emotional and cognitive events that accompany them. Through such careful study, some of the mystery of their problems of living will be illuminated, and patients will collect useful information, which will prove useful in addressing the problem beyond the consulting room.

This approach exemplifies the heart of the behavioural psychotherapies, which are not based on a single approach, far less a single set of techniques. The behavioural psychotherapies articulate general goals in the modification of problems of living, reflecting a set of related orientations to human experience. The relationship between the patient and therapist reflects the patient's relationship with his world: a world of experience, which emerges from the creative interplay of various forces in what Bandura (1978) called "reciprocal determinism". Various cognitive structures and processes, behaviour patterns and their antecedent and consequential environmental events, are all influencing one another in a multidirectional manner. In this appreciation of the 'chaotic order' of the patient, the behavioural psychotherapist finally closes the door on the conditioning theories that gave birth to this exciting "Second Force" in psychotherapy.

Footnotes

[5] Szasz (1967) noted that even Freud practised his own intuitive form of behaviour therapy when he treated a young woman's (apparent) avoidance of feeding her baby; and French (1932) discussed the relationship between conditioning theory and psychoanalysis.

[6] In addition to this Western tradition, there is an Eastern connection. Mikulas (1978) suggested that behaviour therapy and Buddhist thought also shared some affinities – especially the emphasis on operationalism, self-control and the idea of helping the individual control bodily processes to enhance well-being.

[7] Since most psychoanalysts also recognised the role of anxiety, it was Wolpe's approach to anxiety that distinguished him.

[8] Indeed, Wolpe (1978) later acknowledged that his desensitisation had been a cognitive strategy, whilst at the same time viewing cognitive therapists as "malcontents" (Wolpe, 1976).

[9] Mahoney also talked about the therapist being like the "football coach" demonstrating his American heritage.

References

Aristotle (1941) *Basic Works*, translation by Richard McKeown. New York: Random House.

Ayllon, T. and Azrin, N. (1965) The measurement and reinforcement of behaviour of psychotics. *Journal of the Experimental Analysis of Behaviour; 8,* 357–383.

Azrin, N.H. and Naster B.J. (1973) Reciprocity counselling: A rapid learning procedure for marital counselling. *Behaviour Research and Therapy; 11,* 365–382

Bandura, A (1969) *Principles of Behaviour Modification.* New York: Holt, Rinehart and Winston

Bandura, A. (1977) Self-efficacy: Towards a unifying theory of behavioural change. *Psychological Review; 84,* 191–215.

Bandura, A. (1978) On paradigms and recycled ideologies. *Cognitive Therapy and Research; 2,* 79–104.

Barker, P. (1982) *Behaviour Therapy Nursing.* London: Croom Helm

Barker, P. and Fraser, D. (Eds) (1985) *The Nurse as Therapist: A behavioural model.* London: Croom Helm.

Barker, P. (1992) *Severe Depression: A practitioner's guide.* London: Chapman and Hall.

Barker, P. (1994) *A Self-Help Guide to Managing Depression.* London: Chapman and Hall.

Beck, A.T. (1976) *Cognitive Therapy and the Emotional Disorders.* New York: New American Library.

Birchwood, M. and Preston, M. (1991) Schizophrenia. In W. Dryden and R Rentoul (Eds) *Adult Clinical Problems: A cognitive behavioural approach.* London: Routledge.

Brewer, T. (1974) There is no convincing evidence for operant or classical conditioning in adult humans. In W.B. Weimer and D.S. Palermo (Eds) *Cognition and the Symbolic Processes.* Hillsdale, New Jersey: Academic Press.

Dryden, W. and Rentoul, R. (Eds) (1991) *Adult Clinical Problems: A cognitive behavioural approach.* London: Routledge.

Ellis, A. (1962) *Reason and Emotion in Psychotherapy.* New York: Lyle and Stuart.

Eysenck H.J. (1952) The effects of psychotherapy. *Journal of Consulting Psychology; 16,* 319–324.

Eysenck, H.J. (1959) Learning theory and behaviour therapy. *Journal of Mental Science; 105,* 61–75.

Eysenck, H.J. (1987) Behaviour therapy. In R.L. Gregory (Ed) *The Oxford Companion to the Mind.* Oxford: Oxford University Press.

French, T.M. (1932) Interrelations between psychoanalysis and the work of Pavlov. *American Journal of Psychiatry; 12,* 1165–1203.

Lazarus, A.A. (1971) *Behaviour Therapy and Beyond.* New York: McGraw Hill.

Lazarus, A.A. (1973) Multimodal behaviour therapy: treating the basic ID. *Journal of Nervous and Mental Disease; 156,* 404–411.

Lazarus, R.S. (1984) On the primacy of cognition. *American Psychologist; 39(2),* 124–129.

Liberman, R.P., King, L.W., DeRisi, W.J. and McCann, M. (1975) *Personal Effectiveness: Guiding people to assert themselves and improve their social skills.* Champaign, Illinois: Research Press.

Lueger, R.J. and Sheikh, A.A. (1996) The Four Forces of Psychotherapy, Ch 8. In A.A. Sheikh and K.S. Sheikh (Eds) *Healing East and West: Ancient and Modern Psychology.* London: Wiley.

Mahoney, M.J. (1974) *Cognition and Behaviour Modification.* Cambridge, Massachusetts: Ballinger.

Marks, I.M., Hallam, R.S. and Philpott R. (1976) Behavioural nurse therapists: The implications. *Nursing Times (Occasional Paper);* 13th May.

Marks, I.M. (1987) *Fears, Phobias and Rituals: Panic, anxiety and their disorders.* Oxford: Oxford University Press.

Maslow, A. (1962) *Towards a Psychology of Being.* Princeton: Van Nostrand.

Mikulas, W (1978) Four Noble Truths of Buddhism related to behaviour therapy. *Psychological Record; 28,* 59-67

Paul, G.L. and Lentz, R.J. (1977) *Psychological Treatment of Chronic Mental Patients: Milieu versus social learning programs.* Cambridge, Massachusetts: Harvard University Press.

Pavlov, I. (1957) *Experimental Psychology and other essays.* New York: Philosophical Library.

Robinson, D.N. (1986) *An Intellectual History of Psychology.* Madison, Wisconsin: University of Wisconsin Press.

Ryle, A. (1994) *Cognitive Analytic Therapy: A new integration in brief psychotherapy.* Chichester: John Wiley.

Shone, R. (1984) *Creative Visualisation.* Wellingborough, Northamptonshire: Thorsons.

Skinner, B.F. (1938) *The Behaviour of Organisms.* New York: Appleton and Century-Crofts.

Skinner, B.F. (1953) *Science and Human Behaviour.* New York: Macmillan

Szasz, T.S. (1967) Behaviour therapy and psychoanalysis. *Medical Opinion and Review;* June, pp 24–26.

Teichman, J. and Evans, K.C. (1995) *Philosophy: A Beginner's Guide.* (2nd ed) Oxford: Blackwell.

Thorndike, E.L. (1970) *Animal Intelligence: Experimental studies (facsimiles)* Connecticut: Hafner.

Watson, J. B. (1913) Psychology as the Behaviourist Views it. *Psychological Review;* 20, pp158–177.

Wolpe, J. (1958) *Psychotherapy by Reciprocal Inhibition.* Stanford, California: Stanford University Press.

Wolpe, J., Salter, A. and Reyna., L.J. (1964) *The Conditioning Therapies: The challenge in psychotherapy.* New York: Holt, Rinehart and Winston.

Wolpe, J. (1976) Behaviour therapy and its malcontents – II. Multimodal eclecticism, cognitive exclusivism and exposure empiricism. *Journal of Behaviour Therapy and Experimental Psychiatry;* 7, 109–116.

Wolpe, J. (1978) Cognition and causation in human behaviour and its therapy. *American Psychologist;* 33, 437–446 .

Case study 3

COGNITIVE THERAPY OF DEPRESSION

Anne Garland

Jim was 58, had been married for 30 years and had two adult children who lived independently. He described a three year history of depression which followed a constructive dismissal at work. He had worked as stores manager for 20 years when his firm was sold and radical changes in working practices and management styles were introduced. Jim voiced his discontent and came into conflict with senior managers as others were promoted over him. He was forced to take demotion and a wage cut. Work became stressful and Jim took sick leave that led to voluntary redundancy a year later. He invested his redundancy money in a business that subsequently failed.

During our two assessment sessions, Jim described daily problems with early morning wakening, feelings of tiredness and lethargy and poor concentration. These interfered with his ability to engage in activities of daily living and gave rise to procrastination and a loss of pleasure. He described periods of low mood every two to three days, triggered by thoughts of the circumstances surrounding his redundancy and activities not going to plan. Jim had given up his hobbies of fishing and oil painting, and had withdrawn from social contact for fear of being seen as a 'scrounger'. He was involved in a social services – funded working garden, which he attended most days. Before referral for cognitive therapy, Jim had been treated with a therapeutic dose of antidepressant medication, which had proved beneficial in ameliorating some of his depressive symptomatology. Jim did not report any suicidal thoughts and was not considered a suicide risk.

Born and brought up in the suburbs, he described his childhood as "free and easy". He recalled a close relationship with his mother who believed children "should not put themselves forward and should show respect at all times". He described being inculcated with a definite sense of right and wrong, as well as the importance of duty and responsibility. He described his father as distant and critical, as were his school teachers. We agreed a treatment contract of 18 to 20 sessions, twice weekly for two weeks, once weekly for 10 weeks, and fortnightly appointments thereafter.

TREATMENT

The initial treatment session focused on creating a list of problems and targets. Procrastination and loss of pleasure regarding daily activities were given priority for tackling. In the first homework assignment, Jim kept an hourly record of his activities (Activity Scheduling). These were rated on a scale of 0 to 10 for Mastery ("How well I have completed the activity given how I feel") and Pleasure ("How much I enjoyed the activity"). This established a baseline of Jim's activity level, identified links between activity and/or inactivity and mood, and began to identify attributions regarding self, world and future.

Sessions 2 to 6

Jim gave most activity low Mastery and Pleasure scores (between 0 and 2) and he described little sense of satisfaction in his life. Through the use of Guided Discovery and Socratic Questioning, we identified the following attributions:

- He discounted certain activities such as D.I.Y., shopping and cooking as not being achievements and believed that only certain types of activity were of value, namely paid employment;

- He needed to complete tasks to a high standard. This underpinned his procrastination: "If I can't do something properly there is no point in doing it at all";

- He was self-critical of the standard to which he performed a task: "Could do better".

These helped develop our Cognitive Formulation of his problems: "high standards and a striving for perfection in his daily activities". At this point, Graded Task Assignment was introduced and applied to a range of activities. The aim was to increase his activity levels and begin to break down procrastination.

Sessions 7 to 12

These sessions focused on the relationship between Jim's thoughts, emotions, behaviour and biological symptoms at times when he felt low in mood. Although Jim had increased his activity levels, he still reported low Mastery and Pleasure scores and a lack of satisfaction in his life. This appeared to be maintained by his Negative Automatic Thoughts (NATs), which discounted his activities. For example:

▶   "This is a simple task, I used to be able to do it without thinking. Now everything takes ages, I'm useless".

▶   "I don't deserve enjoyable activities, I haven't earned it".

His homework focused on his low mood and associated NATs.

Jim found this difficult, but over three sessions made progress. Often he was angry. Socratic Questioning revealed that Jim experienced persistent NATs regarding the circumstances that led to his depression and redundancy. The theme of unfairness was identified. Jim felt that he had been treated unfairly by his company and had been punished for trying to maintain high standards, which had made him unpopular. His years of loyal service had been disregarded. Three Conditional Rules seemed to have been compromised:

▶   "If you work hard you will be rewarded";

▶   "If you are fair, honest and kind to others, they will be fair, honest and kind back";

▶   "In order to be worthwhile, I must earn a wage".

The origins of these Conditional Rules could be clearly identified as having been laid down and elaborated upon throughout his childhood and adolescence. The first step in the process of modifying such rules was to identify NATs associated with anger and low mood in specific situations, and introduce the process of evaluating them.

Jim found this difficult. Whilst trying to evaluate his NATs, Jim became irritated with me and felt that I was trying to tell him his view of what happened at work was wrong. This led to some exasperation on both parts. Through sensitive discussion, Jim was able to confide that he had difficulty being helped by a "young woman". Attending treatment in itself was a sign of inadequacy and failure, and my proactive style made him feel out of control. Further discussion revealed the importance of control as part of the Formulation, expressed as the Conditional Rule:

▶   "I must be in control at all times otherwise I will lose respect." Jim felt out of control in his daily life.

Sessions 13 to 18

These sessions were used to continue to identify and evaluate NATs and establish behavioural tests to reduce procrastination and develop more realistic standards, and to begin to examine the helpfulness of trying to meet the demands of the Conditional Rules. Particular progress was made regarding his perceptions towards work and his worth being based on the need for paid employment. At this stage, Jim began to socialise more and was less preoccupied with others' views of him. By this stage of therapy, Jim's biological symptoms had improved greatly, and he reported periods of low mood only two to three times per month. He was also more active, and described some improvement in the level of satisfaction in his life.

Sessions 18 to 20

Relapse Prevention was the final stage. This included identifying future situations where Jim may be vulnerable to low mood, and planning how to deal with these. Plans also were also developed to continue to work on Jim's cognitive vulnerability, namely the Conditional Rules.

Case study 4

A COGNITIVE-BEHAVIOURAL APPROACH TO ANXIETY

Richard Lakeman

Psychotherapy is an expensive commodity, often being in short supply. However, many healthcare disciplines can and do employ the principles of psychotherapy in their work, to good effect. I have an enduring memory of a multidisciplinary case allocation meeting, at which the clinical psychologist refused to accept the allocation of a patient on the grounds that he had nothing to offer this person. Nurses seldom have the luxury to pick and choose with whom they work, or find an ideal match between their skills, training, or preferences and patient groups. There is perhaps a lower expectation of nurses' ability to deliver tangible therapeutic outcomes. Under the rubric of 'support', nurses draw upon an eclectic set of skills and knowledge to provide what help they can to those experiencing distress. Invariably, they see their role as only meeting support needs, assessing, or delivering the treatment prescribed by others. Any gains made by the patient are usually credited to the treatments provided by other disciplines.

Nursing can however be therapeutic in its own right, and definitions of nursing proposed by nurse theorists are explicit about the therapeutic potential of a nursing interaction. To realise this potential, nurses draw on a wide range of theory, and research is often not wedded to any particular theoretical framework. Nursing's eclecticism arises in part from the often shallow overview of psychotherapies provided in undergraduate nursing programmes. However, nurses learn therapeutic skills, through personal therapy, clinical supervision, formal study, self-reflection or role modelling, and are challenged to adapt psychotherapeutic skills to the unique context in which nursing takes place. This context is seldom characterised by formal sessions where 'psychotherapy' is the prime agenda.

The context of this case study was a small psychiatric day hospital staffed by a psychiatric nurse (myself) and an occupational therapist. I was not an expert in cognitive behavioural therapy and had little formal training. My knowledge was drawn from reading, clinical supervision and using self-help techniques in my own life. The patient was a 32-year-old woman called Marion, referred to the service for 'support' in managing anxiety and withdrawing from benzodiazepines, which she had been using excessively for some five years.

Marion's medical diagnosis was uncertain. She had previously had limited contact with mental health services, and it had been suggested that she may meet criteria for generalised anxiety disorder, dysthymia, or borderline personality disorder. She was known locally as a "drug seeker" and had only remained in contact with general practitioners (GP) in the region until they refused to prescribe the diazepam that she requested. On the last occasion she approached a GP, three months previously, she agreed to see a consultant psychiatrist, who gradually reduced the dose from 30 mg per day to zero over a three-month period. Although highly reluctant, she was taking no benzodiazepines when she attended for her first interview.

After showing Marion around the small facility, an hour-long interview was undertaken, in which she began to tell her story about her drug use and anxiety. A basic health and social history had already been obtained. Marion made a very good living from doing product demonstrations in supermarkets. She had built this into a successful business whereby she was able to contract out services to a range of companies and employed six other people. Since stopping her benzodiazepines, she had not undertaken any product demonstrations herself; indeed she had isolated herself at home, only doing the minimum required to keep her business ticking over, and she had established a pattern of drinking two bottles of wine each evening to help her sleep. When she had last attempted a product demonstration, she experienced an overwhelming feeling of dread descending over her, with palpitations and breathlessness. Marion urinated on the floor and ran from the supermarket in a state of extreme distress. Since then, she had avoided going into any shops and delegated such tasks to others. She described being unable to relax and feeling faint when exposed to any social situation.

She presented with symptoms of moderate anxiety and mild depression. Over the course of the interview, it was apparent that Marion experienced a number of self-defeating beliefs. Her speech was characterised by over-generalisations: for example, "I'm always stuffing things up"; black-and-white thinking, for example, "It is pointless doing anything if you can't do it well"; an intolerance to anxiety, for example, "I can't stand it when…", and 'mind-reading', for example, "… they think I'm stupid". Additionally, Marion appeared to be extraordinarily fearful of 'losing control' in a public place. She appeared to have difficulty identifying concrete goals for therapy. When we discussed what she was looking for specifically, as an outcome, she could only say, "I just can't go on like this".

Agreement was reached that Marion would attend the day hospital for three days a week over a six-week period. When attending, she would take part in relaxation training and a structured anxiety management group, and meet with her key worker for 45 minutes. In between attendance, she would complete homework exercises set by her therapist. We negotiated the goal that Marion would complete a product demonstration in a supermarket before leaving the day hospital.

On Marion's first day at the day hospital, she appeared extremely anxious and stated that she wouldn't attend unless she could take some medication. In consultation with her psychiatrist, she was prescribed a small dose of buspirone for a one-month period. She was introduced to the ABC model of emotional disturbance in both group and individual therapy sessions. Here she learned how people have emotional reactions at point C (the emotional Consequence) after some Activating event has occurred (point A). However, she also learned that it was not the event (A) that caused the emotional reaction, although it might contribute to it. Instead, the person's Belief system (B) – what the person thinks about the event – is the direct influence on the emotional reaction.

Marion was encouraged to keep a diary of events that happened to her during the day and consequential feelings and behaviour. These were discussed in individual therapy and Marion was coached in identification of automatic thoughts that occurred in response to daily events. Attending groups was initially frightening to Marion, but she quickly identified with a number of women in the small group who had similar problems.

The groups had a didactic component led by the therapist, in which techniques of goal setting, anxiety and time management were introduced. This was followed by practice of techniques, role playing and semi-structured discussion. Group members were encouraged to respond to 'over-generalisation', 'automatic knowing' and inappropriate use of pronouns by asking other group members to be specific. For example, if a group member said "I can never do anything right" another might respond "Can you tell me about one thing that didn't go as you expected?", or they might point out achievements that the person had previously acknowledged. By the second week, Marion was becoming adept at correcting others and was beginning to self-correct her statements within group. Supplementary relaxation training was provided, which involved practising progressive muscular relaxation, visualisation and breathing control exercises in a group situation. Tapes were also provided for use at home, but the expectation was that participants would develop the expertise to use these techniques without external coaching after approximately four weeks of practice and supervision.

After four individual sessions, Marion was beginning to identify automatic negative or distorted thoughts without assistance. She began keeping a diary of events, automatic thoughts and consequential feelings and behaviours. Therapy consisted largely of coaching Marion to identify how these thoughts directly affected her behaviour and feelings.

Activating event	Beliefs	Emotional consequences
The telephone rings.	"It is Joan who wants to hassle me about not attending the meeting. "I will make a fool of myself if I answer"; "She will think I am mad, and that will be terrible".	Does not answer the phone. Feels anxious, depressed and guilty.

One or two extracts from Marion's diary, which she identified as particularly distressing, formed the focus of discussion in therapy. Through the use of a Socratic style of questioning, Marion was engaged in challenging the basis of her automatic thoughts. It became apparent to her that there were recurring themes in her beliefs that led to the greatest distress and disability. These 'core' or 'underlying beliefs' included:

- "I must achieve perfection in everything I do";

- "I shouldn't feel discomfort and pain";

- "Problems have ideal solutions, and it is intolerable when one cannot be found".

An additional task was added to Marion's homework, requiring her to consider the evidence for her assumptions and frame alternative ways of looking at the events. She wrote some alternatives to her underlying beliefs on cards, which she read to herself at least six times a day when she found her anxiety levels increasing, for example, "It is not possible to be perfect in everything that I do, and I am entitled to make mistakes". The cards she wrote were not merely affirmation cards. Marion formulated the statements as direct refutation of self-identified automatic thoughts.

On the third week of Marion's attendance at the day hospital, her mood was greatly improved. However, she continued to spend most of her time in isolation and avoided most of her work duties. She stated that she was ready to "move on" and anticipated that, by selling her business (in response to an offer by one of her staff) and moving to another town and living in modest retirement, she would solve her problems. Whilst her apparent lift in mood was gratifying, it did not appear that her underlying beliefs had changed. Rather, her lift in mood appeared to be related to changing life circumstances. After some discussion, she agreed to complete the programme and recognised that her core beliefs would be likely to surface in the future and cause her difficulties.

Marion was encouraged to prepare a list of activities that she presently found anxiety provoking (in order of severity). Over the remaining two weeks of contact with the day hospital, she engaged in each of these activities – for example, answering the telephone (low anxiety), through to making a mistake in a product demonstration (extreme anxiety). Preparation for exposure to situations involved Marion identifying the worst possible consequences of things not going as she expected, and identifying and refuting the self-defeating thoughts that created anxiety. She was encouraged to test out her assumptions about what people thought about her, in the group, and to challenge the evidence on which her assumptions were based. Homework exercises included deliberate exposure to anxiety-provoking situations and activities that tested her assumptions.

With graduated exposure to anxiety-provoking situations, and using cognitive and behavioural techniques, Marion was able to realise her goal of returning to the practical part of her work. Her alcohol intake reduced as she realised that this was another example of avoidance that she engaged in. She joined a local group of Alcoholics Anonymous. She developed a supportive therapeutic alliance with other group members, and together they engaged in leisure activities such as attending aqua-aerobics classes and accompanying each other to dinner, all of which were previously anxiety provoking.

After five weeks Marion discharged herself from the day hospital and returned to full-time work. She did not sell her business, but rather expanded it to include several larger cities. The therapy and care that she received did not follow a classic 'text-book' style of treatment. It was characterised initially by establishing a trusting relationship and focusing on presenting and anticipated problems rather than past history. The emphasis on homework exercises, and use of adapted cognitive-behavioural strategies, provided Marion with the means to learn more about herself, and how she could think and behave differently. For Marion, much of her anxiety was generated by a fear of failure and anxiety itself. The outcomes of therapy included a re-constituted realistic view of herself that accommodated her human weaknesses, and an increased tolerance to feeling anxious.

4. In search of the person: the humanistic therapies

MAN AS GOD

Psychoanalysis and behaviourism could be criticised for sharing a pessimistic and reductionist views of people, either driven by primitive forces or confined by the laws of learning. The humanistic ideal first developed during the Renaissance, when among others, Ficino observed that,

> "Universal providence belongs to God who is the universal cause… man, who provides generally for all things, both living and lifeless, is a *kind* of god… Man alone abounds in such a perfection that he first rules himself, something that no animal does, and thereafter rules the family, administers the state, governs nations, and rules the whole world" (Cassirer et al, 1948).

These 15th century ideals were probably the first true emphasis on *individualism*, and were neither humane nor humanitarian, but represented what might be called the final stage of chivalry – within which a privileged class might work toward a noble and honourable end (Robinson, 1986). Humanistic psychology, which in turn bred the humanistic psychotherapies, began with an interest in the 'God in Man' and would ultimately be accused, like its Renaissance forbears, of a similar elitism, in its pursuit of the human ideal.

The humanistic therapies emerged in the post-war period, offering the 'baby-boomers' – who were to grow into the 'Me generation' and the hippies – a radically alternative view of the human condition. Carl Rogers (1942), Erich Fromm (1955) and Abraham Maslow (1971) led what was to become known as the 'human potential movement', expressing a shared optimism in the possibilities for human growth. They took to heart Epictetus' dictum that "difficult circumstances do not so much ennoble a man, as reveal him". The humanistic therapies saw the possibility of growth even (or perhaps especially) through adversity. Initially, the movement was very much an American one, influenced by a belief in self-help, originally developed by Samuel Smiles, the Scottish writer who, in 1859, had asserted that "The spirit of self-help is the root of all genuine growth in the individual". A careful analysis of the backgrounds, if not also the 'preaching' of many of the early influences, suggests also the influence of religious revivalism. Some influential therapists came from a religious background, and critics would argue that the whole ethos of 'human potential' was unrealistically optimistic as a result (Marteau, 1976). Although history will affirm that their influence within academic circles was limited, Carl Rogers in particular had an enormous impact on practice, especially in the development of a wide range of counselling and therapeutic approaches (Kirschenbaum and Henderson, 1990). This ranged from "person-centred therapy" (Mearns and Thorne, 1990) to more eclectic approaches (Egan, 1986; Barker, 1997). Indeed, Rogers may well have illustrated which human interpersonal processes were truly necessary and sufficient for therapeutic change to occur.

MANAGING DESPAIR

The humanistic movement had a strong link with psychoanalysis through Erich Fromm, who extended the traditional analyst's interest in 'knowing' about the patient's experience, to studying the experience of 'being' in distress itself. Fromm's emphasis on being linked the movement to European philosophy – especially Heidegger (1967) - and Sartre's existentialism. Fromm's interest also linked humanistic psychotherapy with Albert Camus, who, in the *Myth of Sisyphus,* dealt with the absurdity of life, especially a world in which God no longer existed. The post-war period featured not only the beginnings of the collapse of Western Christianity, but also the escalation of the Cold War and the fear of nuclear annihilation. Fromm believed that, in this new dark age, eventually mankind would have to "face the truth", that he was alone in a universe indifferent to his fate, pushed by a system that has no purpose or goal transcending it (Fromm, 1955). Humanistic psychology and psychotherapy focused directly on the individual, and the fear of alienation in an inhospitable universe. However, it went further, declaring assertively that humankind could benefit from confronting such dilemmas.

IN SEARCH OF UNDERSTANDING

The humanistic psychotherapist's concern to understand people through their own experience led, soon, to the development of a softer – less scientific – approach to human psychology. This feminine emphasis derived, in part, from the influence of Otto Rank (1941), another psychoanalyst who was particularly upset by Freud's patronising attitude towards women. Rank believed that what motivated women was their "emotional and spiritual... craving". That interest was to become a hallmark of the diverse therapeutic approaches developed within the humanistic movement, which prized feelings, and the spiritual dimension, over more intellectual (or masculine) perspectives on humanness. The spiritual interest was to become highlighted for the 'Bomb Culture' generation of the 1960s, which would emphasise the growing sense of spiritual unease within the increasingly affluent West. That unease was linked strongly to a wider appreciation of alienation and aloneness, and borrowed strongly from Kierkegaard the sense that:

> "deep within every human being there still lives the anxiety over the possibility of being alone in the world, forgotten by God, overlooked by the millions in this enormous household" (Kierkegard, 1980: pxiii).

The interest in *understanding* the self was extended further by Viktor Frankl, an Austrian psychiatrist who was the sole survivor in his family from the horrors of Auschwitz and Dachau. Frankl's experiences led him to realise that:

> "there is a fundamental human suffering... which belongs to human life by the very nature and meaning of human life".

Frankl extended this fundamental humanism to his patients, suggesting that we all might:

> "appreciate what an accomplishment there is in the suffering of patients who appear to be struggling – to be worthy of their torment (Frankl, 1971, pp 116)."

Frankl's belief that the distress associated with mental illness was inherently meaningful would be developed later by Laing (1965) and

Podvoll (1991), among others, in their efforts to understand people experiencing major psychotic breakdowns.

The emphasis upon the experience of the self was developed more rigorously by the personal construct theorists (Kelly, 1955). Traditional psychological theories, especially the cognitive and behavioural schools, assumed that people existed only to "process information", to "adapt to their environments" or to "obtain fulfilment or reduce drives". The humanistic therapists assumed that people existed to "make sense of their experience of themselves and their world". George Kelly developed from this assumption the model of "man the scientist" who, from a very early age, tested out the sense she/he made of the world (for example, Bannister and Fransella, 1971; Fransella and Thomas, 1988).

BREAKING THE THERAPEUTIC MOULD

The traditional relationship between therapist and patient, expressed through psychoanalysis and behaviourism, emphasised the authority of the therapist, and the (largely) passive status of the patient. The analyst could be criticised for being detached, and the behaviourist for being manipulative. The humanistic therapist broke this mould with a pronounced emphasis on a quite different relationship, one emphasising empathic warmth, friendliness and the expression of positive regard for the person. Much less attention was paid, if at all, to historical factors, and little interest was expressed in the generation of insight. Instead, the humanistic therapist believed that only through emotional arousal could the person's potential be realised. That emotional arousal could best be facilitated within the client-therapist encounter, where defences against proper relating could be dealt with by confrontation (if necessary) and the assignment of tasks. A wide range of approaches developed around this humanistic philosophy – psychodrama (Moreno, 1948), encounter groups (Rogers, 1970) and various existential therapies, for example, logotherapy (Frankl, 1971). The most well-known and most commonly practised are, however, client-centred therapy (Rogers, 1951) and gestalt therapy (O'Leary, 1992).

CLIENT-CENTRED THERAPY

Carl Rogers was an evangelist turned academic psychologist, who drew to some extent on the theories of Otto Rank, but also incorporated ideas from existential and Eastern philosophy, information processing and group dynamics. He went on to develop his own personality theory, based on research supplemented by his own clinical observations in psychotherapy. In Rogers' view, each person has a "phenomenal field" that determines behaviour. This field shifts from time to time, according to the individual's needs. The aspects of this field that the individual recognises as part of him/herself make up the "self-concept". These include perceptions of the physical body and the person's relationship with others and the world. There may, however, be experiences that the person does not admit to awareness. These are, therefore, disowned, since they are not consistent with the self-concept. This process can result in the creation of tensions, as the person tries to maintain her/his self-concept in the face of a competing set of values. For example, when there is a disparity between a person's ambitions (or the ambitions of others on his/her behalf) and actual accomplishments, defensive mechanisms are brought into play that foster an avoidance of such contradictions. When these defences fail to block such conflicts, Rogers believed that psychosis could develop.

Rogers' great contribution lay in his study of the conditions that were necessary and sufficient for the resolution of such self-concept problems. He recognised that faulty learning lay at the root of neurosis, and emphasised the need to provide the patient with an environment that would not threaten the individual's self-structure further. Such a therapeutic environment would also assist the client to examine, recognise and reorganise the faulty self-concept, "thus permitting an integration of their organism and their self and acceptance of experiences previously excluded as alien" (Wolberg, 1995). The relationship within client-centred therapy offers the person a unique encounter, that involves neither challenge nor condemnation. Instead, every aspect of the person is accepted, allowing the person to yield defences without incurring hurt.

The core principle of Rogers' approach was that the client is autonomous – responsible for her or his own destiny. The therapist holds a core assumption that within each individual, no matter how apparently disabled or limited by problems, lie resources for growth that need only be released to allow the person to achieve human maturity. The work of the therapist involves a gentle form of release, by refraining from imposing any values or patterns on the client, but promoting instead a free expression of feeling.

CORE THERAPEUTIC PRACTICES

Within the therapeutic encounter, the client is given complete responsibility for deciding on the topic or focus of the session, as well as any interpretations associated with it. The role of the therapist is solely to direct the client's attention to what is being said or to ideas or emotions that appear related to the topic. The therapist therefore engages in:

- Careful listening, to establish content and feeling;

- Responding with friendly, empathic comments that neither approve nor criticise;

- Drawing attention to the client's expressed feelings;

- Encouraging the client in her/his efforts to manage problems;

- Offering answers to questions only when absolutely necessary, but avoiding such direction if dependency appears to be developing;

- Refraining from offering advice, criticism, insights or interpretations.

These features of the therapist's behaviour have come to be known as 'non-directive'. Rogers emphasised that the client could achieve her/his own insights within the relationship, and could make constructive use of responsibility. However, any efforts to interpret, evaluate or guide the client towards specific changes were thought to hamper the emergent sense of self-direction and personal growth. In Rogers' view, such a non-directive approach involved a very active focus on perceiving accurately and empathically the client's feelings, and communicating this understanding back to the client through reflection. Truax and Carkhuff (1967) studied the methods developed by Carl Rogers, concluding that whatever else might be offered, people seeking help needed accurate empathy, non-possessive warmth and genuineness. They also recognised the importance of the non-directive therapist's tolerant, non-judgemental way of responding to expressed feelings, which later was defined as 'unconditional positive regard'.

APPLICATIONS AND DEVELOPMENTS IN CLIENT-CENTRED THERAPY

Originally, Rogers suggested that client-centred therapy was most appropriate for people with sufficient personality integrity to solve problems with minimal help from the therapist. Over time, he changed his view, ultimately suggesting that this approach was appropriate for everyone, from childhood to old age, accommodating people with adjustment problems through to psychoses, from any class or strata of society. Today, client-centred therapy is rarely practised in the non-directive way recommended by Rogers, but has developed the exercise of empathy in a more active, participant form. In particular, therapists perceive not only expressed feelings, but also unexpressed feelings, which are experienced 'as if' they were their own.

A major criticism of client-centred therapy is that, although it may be very appropriate for people who respond to caring, non-judgemental therapists, or who are otherwise prepared to change, it may be much less useful for people with other characteristics. In particular, the patient whose problems involve high levels of anxiety may avoid dealing with this problem, and the nurturing, accepting style of the non-directive therapist may compound, rather than address, this difficulty.

Despite these criticisms, the approach to change and growth of human personality pioneered by Rogers has been enormously influential, and Kirschenbaum and Henderson's (1990) view that he "was the most influential psychologist in American history" is almost beyond doubt. It is clear, also, that towards the end of his life, Rogers anticipated many of the developments in therapy that would take place after his death. He wrote, in particular, about the spiritual dimensions of therapy, and the nature of healing of all forms of human distress.

> "When I am at my best, as a therapist... I find that I am closest to my inner, intuitive self, when I am somehow in touch with the unknown in me, when perhaps I am in a slightly altered state of consciousness in the relationship, then whatever I do seems to be full of healing. Then simply my *presence* is releasing and helpful... At these moments it seems that my inner spirit has reached out and touched the inner spirit of the other. Our relationship transcends itself and becomes a part of something larger" (Rogers, 1986).

Rogers' work highlights many of the anxieties that still plague the helping professions. In particular, to what extent should we expect the person to guide his/her own growth and development, or to what extent should we bring our own motivations, strategies, guidance and direction – if not coercion – to that therapeutic encounter? Although to a great extent Rogers' work has been well accepted and embraced, there has also been a great deal of controversy and misunderstanding. His greatest contribution may, however, have been made unwittingly – by adopting an extreme position on the person-centred end of the continuum of caring and helping, he stimulated much of the debate over the control and prediction of human behaviour.

GESTALT THERAPY

This is another popular and influential humanistic therapy. Fritz Perls, who grew disenchanted with psychoanalysis, which he saw as inflexible and too focused on verbal processes and other abstract mental states, developed this approach, which combined influences from Gestalt psychology and group psychotherapy. Perls saw the human personality as a striving for unity (the whole – or gestalt – that symbolised the unification of mind and body). Unlike Rogers, Perls believed that neurosis developed when the person warded off "forbidden trends or blocked-off needs of the total organism, mind plus body". Although gestalt therapy can be practised individually, it is more commonly undertaken in groups, where members watch, learning vicariously, as one individual is assisted towards a fuller, expanded awareness of him/herself.

Perls emphasised the need to engage directly with the patient's feelings:

> "the patient… is instructed to express what he is feeling at that moment to another person. The ways in which he stops, blocks and frustrates himself quickly become apparent, and he can then be assisted in exploring and experiencing the blockages and encouraged to attempt other ways of expressing himself and relating" (Fagan and Shepherd, 1972).

Perls was a rebellious and restless character, who clearly enjoyed the dramatic nature of his encounters with patients. He was also extremely inventive, popularising the use of a range of techniques that have now been adopted by a range of therapists, some only working loosely within the humanistic tradition. Among these were:

- Holding conversations with parts of one's body, people or objects in dreams, or with fantasised people;

- Finishing 'business' with absent (or deceased) people using the 'empty chair' technique, in which the person is visualised as sitting;

- Role reversal, again using the 'empty chair' technique;

- Working in the 'here and now' – emphasising awareness of current feelings (what and how), rather than their remote causes (why);

- I-and-thou talk, in which patients are encouraged to talk *at* others, rather than *to* them;

- The use of 'I-talk'. All references to parts of the body, such as "my chest feels tight", are translated into "I am tightening my chest";

- Exaggeration – where the person is prompted to act out the feeling complained of, in a grossly exaggerated manner.

Not all patients are able, however, to tolerate the drama generated by gestalt therapy, and many therapists also can find the challenging and confrontational style required of them, too demanding. Although many have criticised the gimmicks or melodramatic nature of many of the techniques, some of these have been incorporated into other therapies – especially the emphasis on unfinished business, the empty chair technique and here-and-now working.

Perl's gestalt therapy appeared to embrace, more than any other humanistic approach, the idea of autonomous man, and the need for the patient to assume responsibility for her/his distress. Whereas it is widely assumed that many therapists can employ the principles and techniques of person-centred therapy with only limited training, and with little risk of harm to the client, the same cannot be said of gestalt therapy. The approach not only requires considerable skills and confidence on the part of the therapist, but also carries considerable risk of harming the fragile psyche of the individual patient.

Today, the argument that "counselling doesn't work" is commonly heard, especially by the advocates of randomised controlled trials. This seems a poorly judged criticism, given that there are numerous forms of 'counselling', some employing little more than the "necessary and sufficient" conditions defined by Rogers, others incorporating gestalt techniques, as well as other psychoanalytic or behavioural interventions. More importantly, given the emphasis on 'personal experience', scientific studies are problematic, as the activity of therapy can differ dramatically from one therapeutic encounter to the next. Research may need to turn its attention to what, exactly, might be gained from humanistic counselling that is not available in other forms of therapy.

What appears beyond dispute is that the humanistic school brought a much-needed optimism to the field of mental health. Truax and Carkhuff (1969) noted that "when they (the counsellor) make it possible for others to choose life they increase their own possibilities for choosing life". That characteristic alone may explain the enduring attraction of humanistic counselling, especially for psychiatric nurses who find even today's biopsychosocial 'explanations' of their clientele still a little reductionist (compare Reynolds, 1994). More importantly, the core emphasis on the experience of mental distress has found its way into almost all contemporary therapies through the emphasis on working in the 'here and now', explored through the empathic, warm and genuine therapeutic style first introduced by Rogers. These philosophical and practical legacies of the humanistic school will live on, long after many other forms of popular therapy have been consigned to the footnotes of history.

References

Bannister, D. and Fransella, F. (1971) *Inquiring Man: The theory of personal constructs.* Harmondsworth: Penguin.

Barker, P. (1997) Counselling for behaviour change. In P. Burnard and I. Hulatt (Eds) *Nurses Counselling: The view from the practitioners.* Oxford: Butterworth-Heinemann.

Camus, A. (1959) The Myth of Sisyphus and other essays. New York: Random House.

Cassirer, E., Kristeller, P.O. and Randall, J.H. (Eds) (1948) *The Renaissance Philosophy of Man.* Chicago: The University of Chicago Press.

Egan, G. (1986) *The Skilled Helper: A systematic approach to effective helping.* Pacific Grove, California: Brooks Grove.

Fagan, J. and Shepherd, I.L. (Eds) (1972) *Gestalt Therapy Now: Theory, techniques and applications, Volume 2.* Harmondsworth: Penguin.

Frankl, V.E. (1964) *Man's Search for Meaning: An introduction to logotherapy.* London: Hodder and Stoughton.

Frankl, V.E. (1971) *The Doctor and The Soul: From psychotherapy to logotherapy.* Harmondsworth: Penguin.

Fransella, F. and Thomas L. (1988) (Eds) *Experimenting with Personal Construct Psychology.* London: Routledge and Kegan Paul.

Fromm, E. (1955) *The Sane Society.* New York: Rinehart.

Fromm, E. (1993) *The Art of Being.* London: Constable.

Heidegger, M. (1967) *Being and Time.* Oxford: Blackwell.

Kelly, G.A. (1955) *The Psychology of Personal Constructs, Vols 1 and 2.* New York: Norton.

Kierkegaard, S. (1980) *The Concept of Anxiety,* R. Thomte (Ed and Trans). Princeton, New Jersey: Princeton University Press.

Kirschenbaum, H. and Henderson, V.L. (1990) *The Carl Rogers Reader.* London: Constable.

Laing, R.D. (1965) The Divided Self. New York: Penguin.

Marteau, L. (1976) Encounter and the new therapies. *British Journal of Hospital Medicine; 15,* 257–264.

Maslow, A H (1971) *The Farther Reaches of Human Nature.* New York: Viking.

Mearns, D. and Thorne, B. (1990) *Person-Centred Counselling in Action.* London: Sage Publications.

Moreno, J. (1948) *Psychodrama.* New York: Beacon House.

O'Leary, E. (1992) *Gestalt Therapy: Theory, practice and research.* London: Chapman and Hall.

Perls, F. (1976) Gestalt Therapy Verbatim. New York: Bantam.

Podvoll, E. (1991) The Seduction of Madness. London: Century.

Rank, O. (1941) *Beyond Psychology.* New York: Dover.

Reynolds, W.R. (1994) The influence of clients' perceptions of the helping relationship in the development of the empathy scale. *Journal of Psychiatric and Mental Health; 1,1* 23–30.

Robinson, D.N. (1986) *An Intellectual History of Psychology.* Madison: The University of Wisconsin Press.

Rogers, C.R. (1942) *Counseling and Psychotherapy.* Boston: Houghton and Mifflin.

Rogers, C.R. (1951) *Client-Centred Therapy.* London: Constable.

Rogers, C.R. (1970) *Encounter Groups.* Harmondsworth: Penguin.

Rogers, C.R. (1986) *A Way of Being.* New York. Houghton and Mifflin.

Sartre, J.P. (1948) *Existentialism and Humanism.* London: Methuen.

Smiles, S. (1859) Self-help. Edinburgh: Calder.

Truax, R. and Carkhuff, C. (1967) *Towards Effective Counselling and Psychotherapy.* Chicago: Aldine.

Wolberg, L.R. (1995) The Technique of Psychotherapy (4th ed). New York: WB Saunders.

Case study 5

THE SADNESS OF LOSS AND SAYING GOODBYE

Tony MacCulloch

Larry was a young Jewish student from the United states, who had come to study in New Zealand. He had left behind his family and a dog he was very attached to. His mother was very conscious of appearances, her own and her family. Larry's parents were divorced when he was very young and, when his mother remarried, he liked and developed a close bond with his new stepfather. After some years, his parents separated, and Larry lost the close relationship he had come to value highly.

Larry worked hard to achieve physical fitness and took a real pride in his body. He was a highly motivated, high achieving, outgoing young man. I warmed to him quickly, respecting his commitment to success in his studies and life.

Essential foundations

In our first session, Larry opened: "I wish I could get back to that place where I was fulfilling my potential. I'm being sabotaged and undermined by on-board stuff… that consumes my energy."

He talked of how he had been a major source of support to his fellow hostel residents following the accidental death of another student, who had been a close friend. Larry felt drained by being the giver, feeling "what about me?". He seemed good at giving but less able to receive. During our first session, he asked about my motivation as a counsellor, and if I believed that what he was struggling with could be changed. At this point, we established a flexible contract to explore what was happening in his life, and to discover what needed to change and how that could occur.

We agreed to deal with issues that presented at each session and to follow up themes or issues that needed to be addressed. Larry was clearly committed to the process, keeping his appointments and even notifying me when an unexpected commitment intervened. I concluded that he was very aware and up front, but felt very alone. I was aware of liking him and feeling for his aloneness. He complained of having difficulty with motivation, a theme that was later to be found to be part of a whole range of what could be seen as unrealistic expectations. As I worked with him over 15 sessions, several important themes and needs emerged as ongoing issues to be addressed.

Presenting issues and emerging themes

My initial objective was to establish trust and rapport. I wanted to convey that I was genuinely interested in and concerned for him, really interested in him 'telling his story'. As I listened to Larry, I was able to clarify the surface and underlying issues and themes that were impacting on his life. At the third session, we used an 'issues mind map', drawing on a large sheet of paper, using symbols that represented key issues and themes that had emerged in his story. This enabled Larry to make sense of why he was finding things so difficult. This seemed important in the light of the expectations he had of himself that he should be functioning fully in all areas of his life regardless of events. It was also used to facilitate decisions about which issues he wanted to address first.

Unexpressed and unresolved grief

The typical American culture programmes a range of unrealistic expectations in men. While making daily survival possible, the successful resolution of loss is made very difficult, if not impossible. Staudacher (1991) identified several expectations that Larry demonstrated: being in control; confident; courageous; accomplishing tasks and achieving goals; enduring stress without giving up; and tolerating pain. At the same time, she acknowledged that men are not expected to: lose control; openly cry; be insecure or anxious; express loneliness, sadness or depression; or be dependent. These injunctions were all apparent in Larry at one time or another.

Given his American background, in a family with an emotionally absent father and a mother concerned with keeping up appearances, it was clear that he needed much permission and support to experience his grief and to begin to express it. And it was likely that there was not only the current loss issues to address, but also ones from way back in his early childhood.

Such a past loss emerged later when he talked about an event that occurred when he was 13 years old. As he re-experienced his hurt and sadness, he openly cried. It probably took the seven sessions before this catharsis, for Larry to build the trust he needed to feel and express his hurt and pain, to give himself that permission to cry.

This catharsis was also very evident when, after telling me of two dreams, he connected with the death of his friend earlier in the year. He talked of the trauma, the pain and sadness around the incident. I encouraged him to describe it in detail. Much sadness and tears emerged as we talked of how she had taken a precious part of him away when she died. There seemed so much that was left unsaid, so I suggested we use an empty chair to bring her back to talk to her. He said he would like that but wanted me to talk to her. I sat beside him and asked her to be with us as I tried to put into words the hurt, sadness and pain of that tragic day for Larry. As I spoke, he made additions and agreements between his visible crying. When all that needed to be said was done, we agreed to bid her goodbye.

Larry had confronted parts of himself that had been buried for some time. He was risking letting go of coping strategies that had sustained him to this point. This 'risk taking' is something that the therapist really needs to actively encourage. This seemed to be a significant breakthrough in healing Larry's grief, about this tragedy and also other losses.

Unrealistic expectations of self and others

As I came to understand his upbringing and family, it was not surprising that he had developed a strong 'Critical Parent' ego state that tended to impose rigid and unrealistic expectations. Throughout our sessions, we talked about the basic elements of transactional analysis (TA), to provide a way of understanding what was happening and to provide a structure to guide him as he made changes and decisions.

During one session, he talked of his dog and expressed a lot of hurt and sadness. In the course of doing some two-chair work, it became apparent that it was difficult for him to get in touch with and know what his Child ego state needed in the form of nurturing and support. His own Nurturing Parent ego state was unable to provide any self-nurturing. His Adult ego state asserted his need to make use of the qualities that his sports coach back in America had taught him. Larry had often spoken really highly of this coach, so I invited him to write a list of these qualities. I had noticed that he always carried a back pack on his shoulder, and it seemed that this could become a metaphor for him to take on board and carry with him these important qualities from his coach. At the end of the session, we folded the list into a small package and put it into his bag. This was a symbolic and literal action, to allow him to have and carry with him the qualities that he both needed and valued highly. For me, the symbolism of this metaphor enabled him to internalise the qualities he needed.

At other times, using the TA model, I was aware of helping him to update his Adult ego state regarding the legitimate needs of his Child ego state. This was also intended to empower his decision making and to access his knowledge and wisdom.

In working through and expressing his grief and sadness, Larry was able to reflect on some of his own rigidities and unrealistic expectations. He was able to look at the paradoxical aspects of his attitudes to himself and others, and make decisions to be more tolerant and accepting. This shift had the effect of lessening the impact of his Critical Parent ego state. It also resulted in his taking steps to strengthen his Nurturing Parent ego state and be more aware of, and responsive to, the needs of his Child ego state. I believe that my genuine interest and nurturing attitudes enabled Larry to introject into his Parent ego state some new permissions and strategies for self-nurturing.

Need for nurturing and support

Larry acknowledged his need for emotional support and a discussion venue to facilitate decision making and to talk through things that puzzled and perplexed him.

Seeing him regularly over two semesters provided this support in a variety of ways. Several life and relationship situations presented problems, and we talked them through to a point where he could decide how best to approach them. This was the case when he needed to decide whether to bring his dog to New Zealand. Similarly, the day of the O J Simpson verdict triggered deep feelings of helplessness and injustice, which needed talking through.

On another occasions, when he experienced significant achievements, Larry enjoyed sharing these special moments, knowing that the significance of his success was understood. And I enjoyed sharing his joy and happiness.

This ongoing support provided Larry with a bridge while he adjusted to life in New Zealand. There were clear signs that this was occurring. He started to reach out to make contact with the local synagogue, connecting more fully with his Jewish heritage and identity. Increasingly, he felt more able to connect with and enjoy his friends and colleagues.

Eventually he felt that he had effectively addressed the issues that troubled him and no longer needed to see me on a regular basis.

Reflections on process and outcomes

Throughout my relationship with Larry, I was aware of the precious, almost sacred, nature of such human encounters. I was very aware of the responsibility such an undertaking involves, and at the same time the deep sense of privilege. On occasions, I acknowledged my appreciation of our encounter, and I think he found this self-disclosure affirming and a reflection of his experience.

Later, when I asked him what had sustained him throughout a difficult year, he said "my mates, you, and myself". He talked of how he valued our sessions and the opportunity to say things out loud, and to have himself validated and affirmed as a person. When I asked him what had shifted for him, he talked of how some wounds had been healed, some smoothed over. He said that he had come to accept that some things perhaps never heal fully, and that scars will always remain; but that it was possible to come to a place of acceptance and move on. He also talked of the importance of his move towards reconnecting with his Jewishness and the strength it provided. He had a real sense of the depth and magnitude this spiritual heritage gave him.

Counselling Larry was most rewarding. Both client and therapist are deeply affected by the process of counselling. It is not a one-way process and is not without risk for both parties. The potential for growth and healing of the client is integral to the altruistic driving force that fuels and motivates the counsellor. When Larry challenged me about my motivation as a counsellor, he was I think seeking to establish whether I believed enough in myself and the process of counselling to enable him to believe in himself and the possibility of change and healing. I believe our endeavour together was indicative of this mutual act of faith, trust and risk taking.

Reference

Staudacher B. (1991) *Men and Grief.* Oakland, California: New Harbinger.

Case study 6

HUMANISTIC WORK WITH MEN IN GROUPS

Jon Chesterson

"Shape clay into a vessel;
It is the space within that makes it useful."   Lao Tsu

However we view the world, who we are and how we are to be is much to do with our lifespace. What we pour into this space is what makes life meaningful or useful, and is arguably more important than trying to explain who we are or trying to change this.

In working with people in groups, the accent is placed on reflection and learning through or from personal experience (Kilty 1982; Freire 1972). Thus, the facilitator may influence the conditions that allow change to occur in a way appropriate to the individual and their individual situation, following Rogers' (1967) client-centred approach. While the group becomes the vessel in which life stories are shared, each member attributes their own meanings, sifting the common and diverse elements, deciding choices or changes they might make in the path ahead. The challenge comes from within, where energy flows from self-awareness and active engagement with others, not by coercion or outside rules and mores. The facilitator's task is to attend to meaning, caring, emotional stimulation and executive functioning (Yalom, 1975; Bundey et al, 1988), and to hold personal experience as a valued source of learning.

Men's groups are varied – they may be concerned with parenting and fatherhood, partners of women with postnatal depression or anger management for boys, for example. Each group comes with its own set of agendas and issues to work through. This can range from issues concerning roles, stereotyping, friendship and suicide, through relationships, separation and family issues, to love, sexuality choice and fulfilment. Common themes arise, yet each group creates its own unique space and life.

Given limited time, diversity and the need to attend to participants' needs, we plan and prioritise sessions together, focusing on personal experience, drawing from our own stories, and reflecting upon both old and new meanings. Expectations and issues may also be collapsed by clustering themes, which become the focus and structure of subsequent sessions.

This particular men's group met on a weekly basis for four weeks; each session was two hours long and between eight and 10 participants attended (see Table 1). The sessions were convened to explore together experiences of manhood, seeking ways to build more practical and emotional support into their daily lives. The first session focused on getting to know one another, finding out what had brought them to the group, and identifying key themes and expectations. This provided both a common purpose and a plan for subsequent sessions; structure was only introduced to facilitate exploration of issues raised or reflection on individual life experiences.

Learning through personal experience

In subsequent sessions, participants may be asked for examples of situations they are struggling with. Sometimes we work with the literal description of such an event; at other times we translate it into a mini role play or monodrama. This enables us to get a clearer picture of what is happening, to see how others handle this, and to try out something new, an alternative dialogue. This approach works well in dealing with communication patterns, helping participants to develop listening skills, express feelings, learn to be assertive, handle conflict, confrontation and negotiation, and relate to partners, family, colleagues and friends. There is benefit in giving and receiving feedback, processing the experience afterwards with the whole group.

Learning from the experience of others

When the processes and dynamics of the group are constructive and functional, members can learn from each other. They realise they are not alone in their journey, and that there are alternative perspectives and ways of doing things. It can be helpful to provide an article or book for participants to read, encouraging homework between sessions. Indeed, participants often ask for this, and can be encouraged to bring references, articles, or newspaper clippings that are either topical or of relevance in their lives. This may provide material to talk about – acting as a catalyst – or more information to use in building upon their experiences in the group. Sometimes I prepare handouts: concepts for discussion, a summary of the group's work, processing from a previous session, a synopsis of a useful book or chapter, and a reference list. I introduce relevant concepts, eclectically, for their consideration as a structural intervention (e.g. on communication – principles of assertive interaction, negotiating and confronting, and the art of listening). An example of a synopsis provided as the basis for discussion is summarised in Table 2.

The importance of humour

The best humour comes naturally. Humour is like our appreciation of music and has both personal and cultural meaning and value – therefore sensitivity is important. Humour helps a group relax and lighten up; it reminds us that the we're human. Often it brings us together through our appreciation of others. We are not there to entertain, but humour encourages emotional stimulation. It can also be symbolic, illustrating important points. Recently I received a witty paraphrasing (anonymous) of John Grey's *Men are from Mars, Women are from Venus* (Grey, 1992), which gave me an opportunity to illustrate how different ways of thinking and relating between the sexes influence relationships. This brought forth knowing smiles. Humour is part of the human experience – we learn from it and at the same time it uplifts our spirit.

Learning from feedback

In addition to reflection, feedback is an important way of learning and takes many forms:

- Between participants in response to comments, opinions, values and experiences shared;

- On individual and group progress;

- As affirmation;

- As confrontation;

- Related to the relevance/value of sessions and group experiences;

- As reporting back between sessions;
- On unfinished business from a previous session;
- As personal evaluation;
- As a program/end-of-group evaluation;
- As feedback to/for the facilitator.

Feedback should always be constructive, supporting the process of giving *and* receiving (minimising the influence of personal defences). We need to clarify whether members desire feedback, and allow time for understanding and responses. The importance and meaning of feedback for the recipient is emphasised. Men with few or poor social and emotional support networks receive little feedback and tend to construct their lives in a vacuum. This can be disarming in the face of adversity and life's ambiguities. Also, because of the competitive work, peer and relationship ethic, many men have not experienced the benefits of receiving feedback, may be resistant to it, and may also be limited in their repertoire of giving feedback. Feedback can, however, flow over into our lives, strengthening our relationships and self-esteem. This learning culture is worth nurturing in the group and its potential is not to be underestimated:

Participant: Since the first session [speaking at the fourth], I have got back with my wife after nearly two years of separation, and we are both getting on so much better.

(The other men in the group, were surprised and wanted to know more. Someone asked: What was it that made the difference?)

Participant: Something that was discussed in our first hour, which I thought a lot about afterwards [acknowledging his resistance at the time]... I realised that I had never really listened to my wife, that my communication was one way. I also learned what I could do about this. I am so glad I came.

Facilitator: I am so glad you came back to tell us. This is good... Now that you have found this new ground, what can you do to sustain this?

Learning from experience – visual imagery

The group may be asked to recall a positive encounter with a male parent, teacher, friend or colleague using visual imagery: "What happened, what stood out for you?"

Participant: As a boy, one year I recall spending a string of weekends with my father in our garage, building a motorbike.

Facilitator: What was it about that experience that was important for you?

Participant: Oddly enough, looking back, it wasn't the bike at all. I mean we did a great job. But it was one of the few occasions I'd spent time with Dad, I got to know him better... it was the special time we spent together – felt important, it made me feel good.

Facilitator: How does that affect you today; what does it say about you?

Participant: It makes me feel sort of happy and sad.

Facilitator: Happy?

Participant: Yes... happy when I think about it and when I have those magic moments with our own kids.

Facilitator: ... and sad?

Participant: I don't do it enough with my own kids.

For some, recognising a value that hasn't found its proper place or expression is sufficient. Others may prosper by examining further what is blocking this. Alternatively, others can be invited to share a similar experience, which might help build on this, establishing a common understanding and strengthening the will to change the situation. It's useful to note here, also, the balance between disclosure and vulnerability – knowing when to go deeper, and when to seek others' experiences that may help build trust and cohesion.

Every time we have done this exercise, the group has generated deep human, if not spiritual, values: e.g. spending time with someone, showing special interest in someone, showing compassion or understanding, encouraging others, honest talk, affirming someone's worth, believing in someone, building trust, creating opportunities for others, recognising potential, just listening, being there, and being available. Not surprisingly, some valued experiences centre around camping trips, getting away, fishing, or going 'bushwalk'. Many such experiences involve re-connecting with the natural order of things, which is so often blocked by our busy lives, intellects, 'doing' rather than 'being', getting outcomes rather than appreciating the space. By raising our awareness of these experiences we value, we become aware of the internal tension in our lives, and can learn to accept this, change how we feel about it, or take positive steps to change ourselves and/or the situation.

Finally, we celebrate. Some participants have gone on to form their own support network and group. Some have engaged in an ongoing men's support group. Some have enrolled in other courses/programs such as assertive training and building self-esteem, which they had previously not considered or actively avoided. A few, more experienced, members go on to offer help and support to others, participating in voluntary support programs for teenage boys or connecting with and mentoring other men.

Facilitating men's groups, like other groups, involves creating the space for members to examine what is happening for them. Knowledge and experience aren't the same thing. We often fill the space with knowledge, work, and rushing about getting things done, fixing things. How often do we listen to the voice of our own experience? Sometimes, the simple thing to do is hard: understanding what we are going through often requires us to 'stand under it', allowing the voice of personal experience to illuminate what is front of us. This is the human factor that helps us to centre our lives. This is the space within us that makes the experience useful.

References

Biddulph, S. (1994) *Manhood.* Sydney: Finch Publishing.

Bundey, S. (1988) *Group Leadership: Manual.* Western Sydney Area Health Promotion, (in collaboration with the Institute of Group Leaders), Gungurra Building, Cumberland Hospital, LB 7118, Parramatta BC, Sydney, NSW 2150, Australia.

Freire, P. (1972) *Pedagogy of the Oppressed.* Harmondsworth: Penguin.

Grey, J. (1992) Men are from Mars, Women are from Venus. New York: Harper Collins.

Heron, J. (1989) *The Facilitator's Handbook.* London: Kogan Page.

Kilty, J. (1982) *Experiential Learning.* Guildford: Human Potential Research Project, University of Surrey.

Rogers, C.R. (1967) *On Becoming a Person.* London: Constable.

Yalom, I.D. (1975) *The Theory and Practice of Group Psychotherapy.* New York: Basic Books.

Table 1. Collaborative planning using theme clusters

Session 1
Welcome and introduction; getting to know groundrules e.g. confidentiality, respect; expectations/issues drawn from significant ongoing life experiences; discussion; identifying themes and clustering; planning and prioritising.

Session 2
Communication and relationships (theme cluster 1). Personal experiences/stories (disclosure); discussion (significant or common issue/s and meaning); introducing/presenting helpful concepts; reflection; new possibilities and choices.

Session 3
Unfinished business from last week; feedback (experience/s since last week). **Assertiveness, negotiation and compromise (theme cluster 2)**. Concepts and principles (either drawn from group or interactive presentation); learning through experience, literal description or mini role play (exemplar/s); feedback and reflection; possibilities/choices and hurdles.

Session 4
Unfinished business from last week; feedback (experience/s since last week). **Managing feelings (theme cluster 3)**. Learning from experience, visual imagery; focus and discussion on perception of event, response, values and thoughts that underpin our feelings; how we cope with positive and negative feelings; feedback; evaluation and closure.

Table 2. Key themes in manhood (after Biddulph, 1994)

Seven steps to manhood
1 'Fixing it' with your father
2 Finding sacredness in your sexuality
3 Meeting your partner on equal terms
4 Engaging actively with your kids
5 Learning to have real male friends
6 Finding your heart in your work
7 Freeing your wild spirit

5. Recognising the system: the family therapies

THE FAMILIAL ORIGINS OF HEALTH AND ILLNESS

Traditionally, the psychotherapies have maintained an individual focus, except for occasional forays into group work. The development of child psychoanalysis, and the child guidance movement, introduced the child's family into psychotherapeutic approaches, but the result differed greatly from what we understand today as *family therapy*. Even where relationships were assumed to be fundamental, as in interpersonal psychotherapy (Sullivan, 1953), the clinical emphasis remained with the individual 'patient'. The family therapies broke with this tradition, as they began to explore the family as a unit: first as a *milieu*, then as a *social group* and later, and most importantly, as a *system*.

It has often been said that a family is no more or less complex than an autocracy ruled by its sickest member. Therapists may easily be misled into thinking that the 'primary patient' – the person sent for therapy – is that sickest member. In family therapy, the thorny problem for the therapist involves exploring the complex strategies used (often unconsciously) by families to hide the member who is, truly, the sickest in an emotional sense.

Family life represents a crucible, within which the members forge their relations with one another, often as a response to extra-familial pressure, but often also through replication of the relationship patterns exercised by their parents. This allows the extension of styles of family living from one generation to the next. The notion of the *stable* family, much beloved of advertisers, has a mythical status. Incompatibility between father and mother, however slight, culture or value clashes between parental and social values, not to mention the often inevitable clash between the standards and values of the family and those of the prevailing sub-culture of the children generate complex relationships within the family home. To the family therapist, any problem of living, whether described as neurotic or psychotic, is no more than another event in a family drama. More importantly, such events may represent the way the various 'players' try to maintain a tenuous balance within the family.

In family therapy, the 'patient's' problems are viewed, invariably, as symptomatic of some disorganisation with the family unit. Mother and daughter may challenge, together, the received authority of the father, who seeks his own solution in alcohol, becoming 'a problem drinker'. The same father, threatened by the emergence of his son into adolescence, may subtly challenge him, through unrealistic expectations, driving his son into a schizoid retreat from the world. Since the family unit is the cradle (literally) of health, it should come as no surprise that it can also function as the cradle of illness. However, it is this very contradiction that the family therapist exploits in bringing to bear the family's instinctive drive towards health, as a resource for the resolution of emotional disturbance expressed through one of its members.

It is perhaps no accident that family therapy came to prominence at a period in modern history (the late 1950s) when the traditional values and functions of the family were beginning to be challenged seriously. The conflicting desires for personal freedom and the need for the belonging and security associated with the bonded groups – such as the family – heightened long-standing tensions. Forty years later, such tensions appear magnified and set to grow rather than diminish.

DISTRESSING RELATIONS

Most forms of family therapy can be viewed as an extreme wing of the psychotherapy movement, lying at the opposite end of the spectrum from the intrapsychic theories. Psychoanalysis in particular maintains that symptoms, and resistance to change, lie within the processes of the individual. As a result, it has afforded the family, and relationships, only secondary status. For the reasons already noted, the family therapist views individual symptoms not as 'pathology', but as a meaningful part of the complex network of relationships that serve to create the family itself.

There are, essentially, four forces in psychotherapy, three of which are represented in this book. The psychodynamic, behavioural and humanistic therapies represent the three key voices in defining the form and function of man (sic) and were joined by the voice of the transpersonal therapies only recently (see the Epilogue). Family therapy does not fit easily into any one of these 'forces', since it is defined more by its focus (the family) rather than any overarching theory, that explains what is 'wrong' with the family or how it might be resolved. The family therapist is located within what might be defined, culturally, as a more ancient system: appreciating that change is an ongoing process; and that the individual members of the family, and therefore the family collectively, are changing, whether they wish to or not. This philosophy of living is almost Taoist in orientation (see Watts, 1961). Given this highly alternative stance in relation to human problems and their resolution, it is little wonder that family therapists have often found themselves on the fringes of mainstream psychotherapeutic practice.

Viktor Frankl (1965), who straddled psychoanalysis and the transpersonal therapies, was sceptical about the drive toward self-actualisation, first addressed by Maslow (1968) and which was writ large in the American dream of the 'pursuit of happiness'. Frankl believed that self-actualisation could only develop from the process of living itself, and not as any function of striving. Perhaps family therapists, more than many other psychotherapists, recognised this everyday conflict between becoming and trying, which is so often sorely illustrated within modern families. The unique post World War II phenomenon was of a family focused on developing itself or on aiding its members towards some kind of enhanced quality of life. Today, although family structures appear to be fragmenting, the pressure on individual members to achieve, or otherwise 'keep up', has accelerated. The declining presence of the family, as a buffer against the stress of external societal pressures, appears to leave the profile of the 'individualised' family member even more exposed and vulnerable.

HISTORICAL INFLUENCES

Although a relatively recent therapeutic phenomenon, family therapy emerged naturally from developments in psychoanalysis. Frieda Fromm-Reichman (1948), who had begun to conjure with familial influences in her idea of the "schizophrenogenic mother" developed a decade later by R D Laing and others, was an early contributor. Theodore Lidz (1957) was another key influence, with his description of the parental phenomenon of "marital schism and skew", which he believed contributed to the development of irrational ideas in children. More than anyone else, however, Gregory Bateson and his colleagues were perhaps the most influential, especially with their theory that schizophrenic reactions might be a product of parents "double binding" the child.

Bateson's study of families with a schizophrenic member revealed a 'victim' who succumbed to schizophrenia following exposure to various interrelated factors. The patient experienced (1) a repetition of prescriptive 'themes' or experiences; (2) conflicting injunctions in relation to these themes, with threats of punishment for disobedience; and (3) further restricting commands that prevented the 'victim' from escaping the field of communication (Bateson et al, 1956). In Bateson's view, a mother who felt hostility towards her son might disguise this through overprotection. Although the child might be aware of this, he would not acknowledge it for fear of losing her love. This was, however, a powerful kind of 'victimhood': "the more a person tries to avoid being governed or governing others, the more helpless he becomes and so governs others by forcing them to take care of him" (Haley, 1961). This view of the knot-like family process was developed, most famously, in the work of Laing and Esterson (1964) and later, by Laing himself, in his epigrammatic rendering of the spirals of misunderstanding that can occur within interpersonal relations (Laing, 1970).

Although Bateson's hypothesis has, largely, been rejected, interest in family conflicts in serious forms of mental illness continues to grow. Many clinicians and researchers interpreted Bateson's position as one of laying blame on the family for the plight of one of its members. Researchers continued, however, to explore the effect of family dynamics on 'vulnerable' members – especially the "expressed emotion" work of Brown et al (1972) and Leff and Vaughn (1985), which appeared to show, like Laing and Esterson's work, how emotionally-charged family atmospheres might precipitate relapse in a person with schizophrenia.

PEOPLE AND SYSTEMS

Work with families had been developing since the early 1940s. However, the approach was only acknowledged openly in the 1950s, when some of the pioneers began to publish. The innovative work of, in particular, Nathan Ackerman (1958), Murray Bowen (1976) and Don Jackson (1957) showed great conviction, by challenging the psychotherapeutic conventions of the day. From their work developed a heterogeneous group of approaches: some focusing only on the parents, others on parents and children; some bringing in the extended family whenever possible and even non-family members deemed important to the situation. Perhaps the broadest approach was Speck's *network therapy*, which included family, friends, neighbours, fellow workers and others from the family's community, with groups of as many as 50 people (Speck, 1973). This diversity illustrated the range of freedom that took place within family therapy, which therapists from other schools often found unnerving.

As a result, it is probably more appropriate to talk of a family 'approach' rather than 'therapy', since diversity is a hallmark of family therapy practice. The family therapist does not so much 'treat' the family as arrange conditions under which the family might identify, clarify, gain ownership of, and work towards resolving their own problems. Family therapists reflect a very particular way of thinking about and conceptualising problems. They are interested in what goes on *between members of a family*, rather than what people say is going on *inside them*. This is, perhaps, the most obvious distinguishing feature, and is due to the influence of general systems theory (von Bertalanffy, 1968). The therapist assumes that the difficulties experienced by a family member, or the whole family, is a function of the interaction between those members, and will only be resolved by changes in the behaviour of the persons involved in the "disorganising" behaviour. In conflict with many other psychotherapeutic approaches, the family therapist views such 'problems' *not* as a mere tip of the iceberg – requiring deeper exploration – but the iceberg itself. Therapy often focuses on the solutions that the family has generated to resolve the problem, recognising that these may only reinforce or sustain the interactional difficulty, rather than actually address it.

Beyond these common features, however, lies a plethora of methods, exemplified in three main schools:

- *Structural* family therapy (Minuchin, 1974) addressed the way the family behaves during the session, seeking evidence of alliances between family members as well as the limits of their boundaries.

- *Strategic* family therapy focused on the consequences of bad problem-solving, especially in the form of the presenting symptoms. In addition to exploring existing problem-solving strategies, family members are encouraged to undertake specific tasks, aimed at disrupting some of the existing relations with the family (Haley, 1976).

▶ *Intergenerational* family therapy sought evidence of the fusion or differentiation of behavioural patterns passed from one generation to the next (Bowen, 1976).

More recently, the structure and focus of *behavioural* family therapy (e.g. Falloon, 1991) has become popular, appearing to supplant Minuchin's model. The flowing exchanges of the narrative, in *systemic* family therapy (Anderson, 1991), also appear to have overtaken both strategic and intergenerational approaches.

THERAPEUTIC DIVERSITY

Several other models of family therapy have been developed over the past 40 years:

▶ *Psychodynamic* family therapy focused on unconscious transference distortions among family members, and connections between past relationships and present problems (Bentovin and Kinston, 1991).

▶ *Behavioural* family therapy emphasised the defining of problems as acts, rather than emotions or cognitions. The emphasis is on structured problem solving, and changing the reinforcement patterns between family members (Falloon, 1991).

▶ *Feminist* family therapy recognised the influence of gender, politics and institutions on the form and functions of family life, and focuses on changing the balance of power within relationships, and developing wider access in areas such as choice, opportunity and control (Goodrich, 1991).

However, as noted, two of the most well-known and commonly practised therapies are *structural family therapy,* developed first by Minuchin (1974), and *strategic family therapy,* which emerged from Bateson et al's (1956) communications research. Bateson's analysis of family interaction was developed further by, among others, Fisch and Weakland (Fisch et al, 1983), Haley (1976) and Watzlawick et al (1974).

Minuchin's structural approach focused on answering the question: "how does the family structure maintain this dysfunctional symptom?" This required the therapist to introduce a range of restructuring interventions to transform the dysfunctional family patterns. The family may be encouraged to enact their usual transactional patterns, under the observation of the therapist. The therapist may intentionally escalate stress within the family by blocking the usual patterns of communication, provoking members into adopting or developing alternatives. Tasks may be assigned within or outside the session that facilitate the experience of alternative patterns of interaction. Symptoms may be used directly as the basis for developing new patterns of family interaction. In general, the goal of the therapy is not a change in individual behaviour, but a change in the organisation of the whole family, which may foster new subsystems that will promote healing or growth.

The *strategic* approach assumes that all behaviour is communication and, therefore, it is not possible to *not* communicate. The therapist is not interested in the history of the problem, characteristics of the people (such as personality) or ideas like insight. Borrowing from cybernetics, therapists assume that a vicious cycle has developed from family members' attempts to 'stop' or help problem behaviour. Many of the techniques employed emphasise paradoxical intervention, first developed by Frankl (1960). For example, parents might be encouraged to 'heap even more criticism on the child' resulting in the stimulation of the parents' 'excuses' or 'reasons' for the behaviour of the child.

Although the practice of therapy varies greatly across the various schools, systemic approaches emphasise the experience of the family in the 'here-and-now', rather than in the past. Thirty years ago, Satir (1967) mapped some of the key dimensions of the therapist's role, which included:

- Creating a setting in which the members can risk looking at themselves and their actions;

- Helping members to be unafraid and open;

- Building self-esteem;

- Helping members to become accountable;

- Helping members see the influence of past models on their expectations and behaviour;

- Delineating family roles and functions.

Given the family's experience of difficulty, disruption or illness within one or more of its members, an important aspect of the therapist's role is to reduce threat. This may be achieved by:

- Setting rules for the interaction;

- Structuring the sessions;

▶ Exploring emotional defences;

▶ Careful handling of emotionally loaded material.

When hostility emerges in family therapy, this can easily derail the whole therapeutic process. Often, the hostility is directed at a selected family member, who may be 'scapegoated' or blamed for the crisis that has developed. The therapist needs to interrupt such hostile exchanges, otherwise the status quo will remain. However, such interruptions are complex and formidable tasks for the therapist.

Therapists often handle such tense interruptions by diverting the process, such as asking questions about impersonal areas of family life: housing, routines, work, family history and so on. Where the therapist feels more comfortable, the hostility may be taken up directly by the therapist, asking, "perhaps I have said or done something that has upset you." By opening up such a transference, the therapist may be able to encourage the family to explore their conscious or unconscious motives in making such hostile attacks. This does require, however, a sophisticated therapist, comfortable with his own potential for countertransference.

THERAPEUTIC APPLICATIONS

Systems theory has been used to explain virtually all human dysfunction through relationships, and especially through family relationships. The range of human problems that might, to a greater or lesser extent, be a function of family relationships, is diverse. Social problems – such as child abuse and delinquency; physical problems such as alcohol and drug abuse and chronic illness; emotional problems such as depression and schizophrenia; and relationship conflicts, such as marital disharmony - may all become part of the focus for the family therapist. Although other factors – and systems – play their part in fostering and maintaining such diverse problems, the family represents the most intense and influential system. That said, the power of the family system is not a unicausal determinant of a member's behaviour. Individuals are still recognised as retaining responsibility for their actions: actions that can – and often do – oppose the influence of the family unit.

Although there has been a renaissance of interest in 'family work' within psychiatry, often this has only a limited systemic focus. Behavioural family therapy, emphasising the "psychoeducation" of families with a member with a diagnosis of schizophrenia, is one such example. This appears to be an extension – *ad absurdum* – of Minuchin's assertion that the family needed to be educated by the therapist about the family structure and the dynamics through which the problem is maintained.These models cast the therapist into a high priest or seer role, which other contemporary family therapists view as problematic, both ethically and practically.

Stevenson (1998) has written about the development of her role as a family therapist, away from the educative and manipulative strategies of her youth, and towards a more empowering approach. Developing the "reflecting team process" first described by Anderson (1991), her family therapy team tries to reduce the power hierarchy that split therapists and family members. The team aims for a more collaborative approach, trying to foster new ideas about the problem by setting up opportunities to 're-read' the family's existing stories. Stevenson described how the supporting team members would listen to the therapist engaging the family in conversation. At a mutually agreed point in the session, the family members are offered the opportunity to swap places with the listening team members. The family members, and the therapist who has been engaging with them, now listen to the speculation of the team of family therapists, who reflect openly on what they have just witnessed. Stevenson (1998) believed that this process frees up conversation, by allowing the family members and therapist to comment on what they now 'hear'.

This form of social constructionist family therapy legitimates all the offerings of the family, and is less likely to result in subtle, or covert, redefinition (or reframing) of the original problem. Structural or strategic therapists would be more likely to begin by asking questions aimed at 'discovering' or 'uncovering' some pattern of family dysfunction. The family therapist who works within the social constructionist position described by Stevenson is more likely to begin the session by asking "How would you like to use this meeting?" Such an approach begins by emphasising, from the outset, the collaborative nature of the therapy process. This approach has much in common with the solution-focused family therapy developed by de Shazer, (1982), discussed in the next chapter (Chapter 6).

THE SPIRIT OF THE FAMILY

It has become a systemic cliché to claim, with reference to the family, that the whole is greater than the sum of its parts. Musical notes on a page are not the piece of music, but require to be 'organised' by an orchestra. Similarly, the family is not just a collection of people, but also encompasses the way they are organised. The experience of family membership – contributing to both the 'melody' and the 'discord' – involves being musician, instrument and composer, all in one. Little wonder that the process of exploring and explicating the composition of family relationships can often be complex.

Virginia Satir (1988) is one of the most famous of family therapists. She described how, because she was a woman *and* a non-medical therapist, the only people she could work with, at first, were the 'rejects' from other therapists, high-risk people who had been abused, or were alcoholic, psychopathic, or otherwise viewed as untreatable. However, she found that many of these people began to blossom as the therapy progressed. In Satir's view, this was because:

> "I was working to contact their spirits, loving them as I went along. The question for me was never whether they had spirits, but how I could contact them. This is what I set out to do. My means of making contact was in my own congruent communication and the modelling that went with it... I consider the first step in any change is to contact the spirit. Then together we can clear the way to release the energy for going toward health. This too is spirituality in action." (Satir, 1988; pp 340-341)

Satir's view suggests the possible direction that family therapy might be taking: helping the family to explore its own ineffability – the internal dimension of the family that might well lie beyond the gaze of any therapist, but that is fully within the sights of all of its members.

These systemic views remain largely peripheral to psychiatry, which appears to focus more and more on 'individuals' and their pathology. Psychiatry's search for explanations and answers to people's human problems increasingly emphasises what is going on within the individual's physical or psychological 'selves'. However, as mental healthcare is established more firmly in the natural community, we have another opportunity to focus on the natural complexity of human problems, especially within the human cauldron of experience that is the family.

References

Ackerman, N. (1958) *The Psychodynamics of Family Life.* New York: Basic Books.

Anderson, T. (1991) *The Reflecting Team: Dialogues and Dialogues about the dialogues.* New York: W.W. Norton.

Bateson, G., Jackson, D.D., Haley, J and Weakland, J.H. (1956) Towards a theory of schizophrenia. *Behavioural Science; 1,* 251–264.

Bentovin, A. and Kinston, W. (1991) Focal family therapy: Joining systems theory with psychodynamic understanding. In A.S. Gurman and D.P. Kniskern (Eds) *Handbook of Family Therapy Vol 2.* New York: Brunner Mazel.

Bowen, M. (1976) Theory in the practice of psychotherapy. In P. Guerin (ed) *Handbook of Family Therapy.* NY: Gardner Press.

Brown, G.W., Birley, J L T and Wing, J. (1972) Influence of family life on the course of schizophrenic disorders: A replication. *British Journal of Psychiatry; 121,* 241–258.

de Shazer, S. (1982) *Patterns of Brief Family Therapy.* London: Guilford Press.

Fisch, R., Weakland, J.H. and Segal, L. (1983) *The Tactics of Change: Doing therapy briefly.* San Francisco: Jossey-Bass.

Frankl, V. (1960) Paradoxical intention: A logotherapeutic technique. *American Journal of Psychotherapy; 14,* 520-535.

Frankl, V. (1965) *The Doctor and the Soul: From psychotherapy to logotherapy.* New York: Knopf.

Falloon, I.H. (1991) Behavioural family therapy. In A.S. Gurman and D.P. Kniskern (Eds) *Handbook of Family Therapy Vol 2.* New York: Brunner Mazel.

Fromm-Reichman, F. (1948) *Principles of Intensive Psychotherapy.* Chicago: University of Chicago Press.

Goodrich, T.J. (1991) Women, power, and family therapy: What's wrong with this picture? In T.J. Goodrich (Ed) *Women and Power: Perspectives for family therapy.* New York: W.W. Norton and Co.

Haley, J. (1961) Control in psychotherapy with schizophrenics. *Archives of General Psychiatry; 5,* 340–353.

Haley, J. (1976) *Problem-Solving Therapy.* San Francisco: Jossey-Bass.

Jackson, D.D. (1957) The question of family homeostasis. *Psychiatric Quarterly Supplement; 1:* 79–90.

Leff, J.P. and Vaughn, C (1985) *Expressed Emotion in Families: Its significance for mental illness.* New York: Guilford Press.

Laing, R.D. (1970) *Knot.* Harmondsworth: Penguin.

Laing, R.D. and Esterson, A.A. (1964) *Sanity, Madness and The Family.* London: Tavistock Publications.

Lidz, T. (1957) The intrafamilial environment of the schizophrenic patient: Marital schism and marital skew. *American Journal of Psychiatry; 114,* 241–248.

Maslow, A. (1968) *Toward a Psychology of Being.* New York: Van Nostrand.

Minuchin, S. (1974) *Families and Family Therapy.* Cambridge, Massachusetts: Harvard University Press.

Satir, V. (1967) *Conjoint Family Therapy.* Palo Alto, California: Science and Behaviour Books.

Satir, V. (1988) *The New Peoplemaking.* Mountain View, California: Science and Behaviour Books.

Speck, R.V. (1973) *Family Networks.* New York: Pantheon Books

Stevenson, C. (1998) Trying to treat the system: Dominance and negotiation in family therapy. In P. Barker and B. Davidson (Eds) *Psychiatric Nursing: Ethical strife.* London: Arnold.

Sullivan, H.S. (1953) *Conceptions of Modern Psychiatry.* New York: Norton.

Von Bertalaffny, L (1968) *General Systems Theory.* New York: George Braziller.

Watts, A. (1961) *Psychotherapy East and West.* New York: Pantheon Books.

Watzlawick, P., Weakland, J.H. and Fisch, R. (1974) *Change, Principles of Problem Formation and Problem Resolution.* New York: W.W. Norton and Co.

Case study 7

A FAMILY-BASED APPROACH TO PSYCHOTIC BREAKDOWN

Kate Bones and Una Hunt

The Faiths were referred for family therapy through psychiatric out-patients. Joanne (the identified patient) reported increasing conflict between herself and her family ever since her first psychiatric breakdown some 10 years previously. Joanne felt specifically that her mother had neglected her during the early stages of her illness, which manifested itself as a psychotic breakdown whilst she was working as a teacher in Spain.

Following the breakdown, Joanne returned to Britain and moved back into the family home. However, her behaviour became so disruptive that she moved out into a hostel for homeless people, to the relief of her family. She then deteriorated further, and spent some time sleeping rough before being admitted to a psychiatric hospital under the Mental Health Act in 1985.

Joanne still harboured deep resentment towards her family, especially her mother, who she felt was unsympathetic and uncaring. Paradoxically, she had a fixed arrangement that her mother would come to clean her flat every fortnight, despite her mother having to look after her frail 79- year-old husband.

Family therapy using the systemic model can be understood as consisting of three main phases. Although the distinction between these phases is blurred, it is useful to think of family therapy as containing these interdependent dimensions occurring simultaneously over the period of treatment.

Assessment

This includes determining relevant behavioural patterns and belief systems in the family. In the case of the Faiths, predisposing factors included a history of unresolved issues in the recent and distant past. Joanne felt that her family had failed to notice when she was becoming ill. She also felt that this neglect had led to a deterioration in her condition, and had resulted in her present level of chronicity.

The family, however, felt that they had made numerous attempts to get Joanne to see a doctor, but she was very rejecting of all forms of help, especially while she was homeless.

Now that Joanne was settled in a flat, Mrs Faith felt that Joanne still felt resentful toward her, and through resulting feelings of guilt, she was taking responsibility for cleaning Joanne's home. Joanne, through this act, continued to define herself as vulnerable, and saw this as proof that her mother 'owed' her something for her past neglect.

The initial goals of the assessment period were as follows:

- To determine how the family thought in the sense of a singular unit i.e. what themes are present;

- To encourage the family to discuss their views of the presenting problems with each other, thus allowing us to observe the communication patterns that occurred during the process.

Instilling doubt

This process is used to alter presenting perspectives and to introduce some flexibility into a rigid belief system.

For the Faiths, this meant casting doubt on the validity of the family's common belief system about the problems Joanne blamed her family for.

Patterns of change

This phase of therapy is characterised by implicit or explicit requests for change in the patterns that are associated with the presenting problem.

For this family, this meant making decisions about what needed to be changed, and deciding how to shift the belief structure to allow the desired behaviour to occur. This links the three aspects of treatment together.

Case illustration

An early session began with both Joanne and her mother reviewing events surrounding the Easter period, which they had spent together. Initially they focused on negative events, highlighting areas of conflict and disagreement.

The intervention was for them to look for exceptional events or situations where they felt they had communicated well or enjoyed each others' company. In order to elicit this response, I used circular exploratory questions, aimed at shifting the perspective away from the individuals, in order to concentrate on the interactions and their context (assessment).

Later on in the session, the family began to discuss issues of dependence versus independence. The issue of asking for help or appearing vulnerable in the family was problematic; things were viewed in 'all or nothing' terms, and one was either independent or dependent.

I then tried to help the family to reframe the perception of Joanne being neglected at the time of her initial breakdown – a dependence versus independence issue in the family system. I suggested that Joanne was the victim of a mutual misunderstanding because of the family's own value belief system about independence. This rigid belief system meant that the family had not developed a mutual way of asking for and receiving help (instilling doubt).

I then prompted the family to use this insight to plan how they would spend time together in the next few weeks (pattern of change).

Over further sessions, it became apparent that the family relied on key 'symptoms' to maintain a homeostatic balance within the family system. This centred around Mrs Faith cleaning Joanne's flat. In light of this, I highlighted areas in which the family had improved in their ability to communicate with each other, and asked them to think about what else, if anything, they wanted to gain from the sessions. I felt there was little to gain therapeutically from trying to shift a family system too far, when the family was clearly unable to make that move.

Conclusion

Joanne remained angry with her mother, but overall communication patterns within the family had improved to a level where there were more positive interactions and fewer expressions of open conflict. My main role at the end of therapy was to help the family draw up a kind of 'peace plan', where the family members negotiated compromises and explored ways of resolving problems before they became unmanageable.

Case study 8

AN ECLECTIC APPROACH TO A FAMILY IN TRANSITION

Phil Barker

Life is lived as drama – sometimes comic, often tragic, but always dramatic. That simple fact may explain the attraction of the soap opera, which reflects some of the surface of ordinary life, or the enduring appreciation of Shakespeare, who depicted the intricate weave of love and death, power and madness. Family therapy usually focuses on the nuclear family – parents and their children. However, often in-laws, close friends and even neighbours are also part of the family drama. In the case illustrated here the key players were the two surviving members of the nuclear family, supported (dramatically) by a son-in-law (who rarely spoke) and a neighbour. The approach adopted by the therapist was primarily *strategic*, but was augmented by some interventions drawn from psychodynamic therapy.

Mrs Black had lived alone since her husband's death, 10 years earlier. Her only daughter, Caroline, had been surprised at how well her mother had coped. "Mum was always so dependent on him... always having to be

home to make his tea... seeing him off to the office... that kind of thing."
Over the past two years Mrs Black's physical health had declined and
there were now signs that her memory was also failing her. The
neighbours had even reported 'sightings' of her wandering in her night-
gown in the early hours. Although her husband had been a lowly shipping
clerk, Mrs Black "put on airs and graces", which irritated her daughter,
who although a graduate, described herself as "still working class". She
was, however, well-respected by her immediate neighbour, Mr Jackson,
who took Mrs Black shopping each week: "'Mrs Black is the only council
tenant left, we've all bought our homes, but the old dear, she has more
class than most of the rest of the avenue. Ironic, ain't it?"

Caroline lived about 10 miles away, with her husband Richard. They were
both only children and were childless, but stated that "we got over that...
we're not alone." Initially, as her mother showed signs of deterioration,
Caroline and Richard had visited more often. In the last few months,
Caroline had been off work with "some kind of stress" and the GP, who
also visited her mother, referred them both to the Community Mental
Health Team.

The therapist saw Caroline alone at first. She was tearful, yet angry, as she
talked almost continually about her mother, and how her mother needed
to "pull herself together, or else they'll put her away". She dismissed her
own problems as menopausal and "pure stress". She was aware that her
mother had also been referred and agreed to meet the therapist at her
mother's house the following week.

Mrs Black was going to and from the kitchen with an empty teapot when
the therapist arrived. She offered him some tea and laughed when she
found the pot empty. There was a muffled but heated exchange between
Caroline and Mrs Black in the hallway, when Richard entered. He ignored
his wife and mother-in-law but introduced himself to the therapist, then
retired behind a newspaper.

When Caroline and her mother returned with the tea, Mr Jackson was
with them, carrying a plate of cakes on a tray. After a further round of
introductions and more tea, the therapist turned the page of this
domestic drama.

T: Perhaps we could begin by talking about how things are. Now I mean, right now. OK?

After a brief silence, Mr Jackson spoke.

Mr J: Well, Dora – Mrs Black, I mean – has been up against it of late, haven't you dear? I mean, we're not getting any younger [laughs].

Mrs B: straightened herself and sipped her tea slowly. Caroline sat back and folded her arms.

C: See what I mean… it's what I've always said… she won't own up to anything, still putting on airs and graces, just because there is a 'gentleman' in the house… she makes me so mad… I could scream… she's… [Unfolding her arms and breaking off suddenly] Richard, there's no more milk. Please?

Richard rose quickly, leaving the group to sit in silence. Mrs Black, erect, looked out of the window.

T: Mrs Black. Caroline appears angry with you. How did you feel when she said she could scream just now? What do you think she means when she says you won't own up to anything?

Mrs B: (turning slowly – looking directly at the therapist): She is highly strung, always has been… I try to ignore her… best thing I think… least said, soonest mended.

C: (Interrupting) See… there she goes again… pure denial, denial, denial.

T: (To Caroline) Talk with your mother about that.

C: What? What do you mean?

T: I think that is for your mother, not me. Talk to your mother about that.

In that first meeting, the therapist encouraged the family and Mr Jackson to focus on the 'here and now', inviting them to address what was happening (emotionally) there and then. This provided the 'story', that was threaded, invisibly, through the human drama being enacted. The therapist alternated this with encouragement to talk with one another, often directing them to talk about specific things they had raised, or asking individuals specifically to express their feelings. He assumed that whatever was a 'problem' might well have been an interpersonal difficulty that had escalated as they had tried (unsuccessfully) to solve it. By directly prompting the group to engage in different patterns of interactions and emotional expression, the members began to restructure their inter-actional patterns. Gradually, the mood of this augmented family changed.

The extent to which all four people present were 'in role' became clear as each began to experience new feelings and they suspended the usual rules of relating to one another. Mr Jackson spoke of his fears that he might be "in the same boat" as Mrs Black soon, and Richard slowly stepped out of his strong wife's shadow to express some of his disappointment at what he saw as "my failure to give Dora the grandchild she always wanted". "And what about Caroline's child?" the therapist asked, "and what about you?"

Caroline and Mrs Black clung more firmly to their original roles, but were reduced first to tears, then laughter, when Richard launched a furious and unprecedented torrent of abuse at both of them. The worm who had turned smiled almost smugly as he realised that his years of enforced calm had been working against him.

The therapist came and took tea with this small group for two months, Caroline and Dora invariably taking the dramatic 'leads'. By the time he finally took his leave of them, mother and daughter had experienced some of the comedy in the mini tragedies they had unwittingly created. Mrs Black remained erect and haughty, but when the therapist asked "Does your daughter love you, do you think?" she smiled broadly, "Of course she does, as I do her. It's just our way, isn't it? Of course it is."

Mrs Black continued to deteriorate, but the drama that went on around her appeared to have a new playwright. Gone, to a large extent, was Caroline's irritation, with its concomitant stress. Gone were many of Dora's airs and graces. Mr Jackson would hear Caroline shouting (often swearing) at her mother, "and Dora just smiles, you know, old devil." Richard never looked more comfortable as he watched the racing on the old black-and-white television, speaking (only) when he had something to say.

Mrs Black eventually did go into a home. Caroline and Richard visited her every week and continued seeing Mr Jackson who too was beginning to fail. As they drove home, they would talk about being the "end of the line". Sometimes, Caroline would ask Richard if he felt sad, like her, and he would smile and say "of course I do, but it'll pass... most things pass, don't they?"

6. Loosening the knot: the solution-focused psychotherapies

THE PARADIGM SHIFT

The beginning of the 1980s witnessed the emergence of a new school of therapy. *Solution-focused* psychotherapy[10] has a short, yet complex lineage. In part, it developed from strategic therapy (Weakland et al, 1974), which in turn grew out of various developments in family therapy – the influence of Bateson and his colleagues' work into the family "construction" of schizophrenia (Bateson et al, 1956). It was also influenced by the maverick hypnotherapist Milton Erickson (Rossi, 1980).

Although Erickson refused to identify himself with any specific school of psychotherapy, analysis of his casebooks shows how he integrated cognitive, analytic and behavioural methods with his own unique and charismatic style of relating to patients. Erickson's philosophy was simple: psychotherapy should aim to liberate the potential for self-help in the patient, and this could be done in either the hypnotic or waking state. Invariably, such interventions were brief, aimed at developing solutions to problems, and avoided exploring the problem in any depth. Erickson recognised the uniqueness of each patient, emphasising the need to offer an original mode of therapeutic response, rather than some doctrinaire, orthodox methodology. From his hypnosis work, Erickson developed a style of interviewing that showed how the patient's language could be employed to construct cognitive solutions to his problems, which could then be enacted in assignments directed by the therapist.

Although other psychotherapists had emphasised ways of enlisting the patient's[11] involvement in generating solutions to problems, psychotherapy in the 1970s was still a problem-oriented undertaking. Although other psychotherapists worked with language, generally it was assumed that language represented the reality of the patient's experience, which was the real focus of attention. The Palo Alto group in the United States began, like Erickson, to explore the *structure* of language, and the part it might play in constructing solutions to the patient's problems (Watzlawick, Weakland and Fisch, 1974; Watzlawick, 1978). It began to dawn on these psychotherapists that, although an understanding of 'the problem' might help appreciate its genesis, a different understanding might be necessary to understand 'the solution'. Here occurred the crucial break with the structuralist tradition, which had defined the language of science and of psychotherapy up to this point.

The increasing concern over the financial cost of therapy had encouraged several schools of psychotherapy to emphasise the brevity (and therefore cost-efficiency) of their interventions: for example, brief psychodynamic psychotherapy. However, the principles and techniques of solution-focused brief therapy (SFT), first described over a decade ago (de Shazer, 1985), involved a significant departure in psychotherapeutic theory and practice. Although SFT represented a range of approaches rather than a single method, it embraced a distinctive philosophical outlook: radical constructivism. Rather than adopting any psychological theory (or ideology), constructivism (or post-structuralism), appeared to be the basis of the therapy, leading Gergen (1992) to describe it as the first post-modern therapy.

A POST-STRUCTURALIST PSYCHOTHERAPY

Various writers (for example: Von Foerster, 1984; Von Glaserfeld, 1984; Watzlawick, 1984 and Maturana and Varela, 1987) had proposed that, rather than being "out there", reality was "constructed", arguably "in here", within the person who was talking about "reality". How people performed this construction depended on the "lenses" through which they viewed, and made distinctions about, themselves and the world (Walter and Peller, 1996). Consequently, solution-focused therapists assumed that since patients had 'constructed' their problems they could construct their solutions.

Structural thinking is the basis of the accepted scientific view of the world: something 'out there' can be measured and studied, with a view to generating predictive theories about events 'in' that world. Structuralist psychotherapists – in particular psychodynamic and behaviour therapists – aim to *know* the human world of the patient, uncovering it by detailed observation, analysis *and* interpretation, within a specific frame of reference – their guiding theory. Traditionally, psychotherapists have looked for the truth beneath the surface structure of "what the patient says"; exploring the sub-text; reading between the lines of his narrative.

The post-structuralist position, which embodies the solution-focused approach, acknowledged that it is useful (if not vital) to take the physical world 'apart' when, for instance, looking for a fault in a car engine. Human problems – such as low self-esteem or depression – are, however, qualitatively different. In Watzlawick's view, it is not the case that people 'are' or 'are not' *depressed*, rather the truth of the person's situation is negotiated through dialogue – meaning is invented rather than discovered (Watzlawick, 1984). The key theorist within the practice of solution-focused therapy, de Shazer (1991), has argued that "meaning is here open to view since it lies between people rather than hidden away inside an individual (pp 45)". In his view, if there is not enough information in what the person says to establish what a resolution of their problem would involve, the therapist should ask more questions about this future state and listen more carefully: "what will be different when you are no longer depressed?" rather than "how did you become depressed", or "what depresses you?"

This view of the co-creation of reality is not only incompatible with the structuralist position, but in Harland's (1987) view is also "radically anti-scientific". Hawkes, Marsh and Wilgosh (1998) recognised that the solution-focused approach can appear to be psychologically "agnostic", since – unlike other therapies – it does not hold to any psychological theory about personality development (or ideology). Indeed, the solution-focused therapist is uninterested in causation, but assumes that the construction of the solution need have no relationship with the 'cause' of the problem. This philosophy is manifestly influenced by some of Wittgenstein's views of language (Wittgenstein, 1958), but also shares a remarkable affinity with Eastern philosophies, such as Taoism. Watts (1961) described Taoism as a "way of life" that should be seen more as psychotherapy than a religion. Taoism acknowledges that stability in life is an illusion and is a function of memory rather than reality. Life (Tao) 'flows' through people producing incessant change, of which, in general, people are unaware. Solution-focused therapy may simply draw patients' attention to this flow of change, helping them steer in one direction rather than another (Barker, 1996).

Given these philosophical assumptions, the roles of the therapist and patient in SFT are very different. In traditional forms of therapy, the therapist observes, interviews, and gives the patient information and feedback, often making interpretations of the patient's story. In SFT, it is assumed that the patient's story is, rather than represents 'reality'. De Shazer (1994) suggested that talk (or language) is all that can be focused on within therapy:

> "There are no wet beds, no voices without people, no depressions. There is only *talk* about wet beds, *talk* about voices, *talk* about depression. There are no family systems, no family structures, no psyches: just talk about systems, structures, and psyches"(1993).

As a result, patient and therapist are involved in a process of mutual meaning-making. The traditional therapeutic language of observation, interview, interpretation and so on are replaced by the language of conversation, narrative, reflections and text.

A MODEL OF QUESTIONS

The way that the therapist seeks to *understand* the patient – by listening (only) to what is said – embodies the solution-focused, therapist-patient relationship. It is also illustrated by the kind of questions the therapist asks, and also doesn't ask – what the therapist says and does, as well as *avoids* saying and doing.

SFT has been called the "model of questions" (Miller, 1995). In traditional therapy, questions are asked with a view to gathering information as part of the assessment, validating a hypothesis, solving problems or trying to be helpful. In SFT, such practices are shunned. It is assumed that, by emphasising the patient's 'view', meaning will emerge. Consequently, the therapist does not hypothesise – in advance – as to what might be the 'problem', far less the 'solution'. Similarly, the therapist avoids hypothesising during the session. O'Hanlon has noted repeatedly that every therapist's office should have a couch, so that whenever he feels a hypothesis coming on, he can lie down until it goes away! These assumptions lead, directly, to the kind of questions asked, all of which aim to establish:

- What does the patient *want* from therapy?

- How will this make a *difference* for the patient?

- How will the patient *know* that a problem is being solved, or that she/he is 'on track'?

- How is the patient *experiencing* something of what she/he wants *now*?

More specifically, the therapist asks about:

- *Exceptions:* What is *different* when the problem is not evident?

- *Coping:* How the patient keeps going, carries on living, or isn't 'worse' given the presence of the problem.

- *Scaling:* Where is the patient at present, on some hypothetical scale of 'severity,' 'change', or 'movement'?

- *Miracles:* What would the patient notice if a miracle resolved the problem?

- *The future:* What will the patient do when the problem is no longer troubling her or him?

- *Resources:* How did the patient work that out? How did he know that?

Unlike the traditional therapist, the solution-focused therapist does not ask about patients' histories – how long they have had a problem, how they think that they 'got' the problem, or what might have 'caused' it. Since the 'causes' of problems are assumed to have little bearing on the construction and attainment of solutions, all such talk is of limited value.

OPTIMISTIC THERAPY

These questions assume also that the patient brings specific personal assets, or strengths, to therapy – this began with seeking, or agreeing to enter, therapy. It also acknowledges that the patient has already made many attempts to resolve the problem, although the patient may well not acknowledge this. The therapist attempts throughout to re-connect patients to *their* own abilities to resolve *their* own problems.

Essentially, the therapist recognises that the patient, not the therapist, is the expert. Although this has some parallels with Mahoney's (1974) personal science model (see Chapter 3), the solution-focused therapist tries to 'stay dumb' long enough to allow the patient to generate his own solutions, rather than proffer technical advice. Hawkes et al (1998) noted that other psychotherapists – even psychoanalysts – have tried to respect the authority of the patient:

> "I think I interpret mainly to let patients know the limits of my understanding. The principle is that it is the patient and only the patient who has all the answers"(Winnicott, 1971, pp 84).

Traditionally, psychotherapists provide 'feedback', pointing out the patient's faults, weaknesses or omissions, whether manifest or interpreted. Feedback in SFT usually involves compliments or exclamations of surprise at how well the patient is doing; or otherwise being impressed by evidence of change, difference, exceptions to the problem or successes (however small) and personal resourcefulness. Such feedback validates aspects of the patient's personal functioning.

The solution-focused therapist does *not* make interpretations. This would suggest that the therapist might have a better understanding of the problem, or even of the patient, thus breaking the 'patient-as-expert' rule. Equally, the therapist does not challenge the patient's selection of goals, or recommend more sessions of therapy. Traditionally, therapists – especially within the medical framework – have ranked patients according to some hypothetical scale of difficulty. People with neurotic disorders have been viewed as straightforward (the 'worried well'), while people diagnosed with schizophrenia, manic depression or personality disorders occupy the other extreme (the 'seriously mentally ill'). Solution-focused therapists eschew such distinctions, assuming that complex problems do not always need complex solutions. The therapist is interested in what would represent a solution to a problem *for the patient*. As a result, the therapist is not 'treating' depression, schizophrenia or any other such disorder, since these represent professional constructions placed on people and their problems. As a rule, the therapist will accept the patient's ideas about a solution, providing that this does not cause any ethical or legal complication, or is not manifestly dangerous for either party. Like some therapies influenced by Eastern philosophy, such as *Constructive Living* (Reynolds, 1984), simple solutions – like walking more, talking to different people, or smiling intentionally – may help to change apparently complex problems.

RESPECTFUL THERAPY

Much of what takes place within the session could be described as 'mapping'. The patient has reached a certain point in his life and needs to establish where (exactly) he goes next. As noted earlier, acknowledging where he *has been* (past history) in his life may be interesting, but is not a necessary requisite for establishing where he goes next. To paraphrase the Chinese saying: "The journey of a thousand miles begins under your very feet". Therapy focuses on the steps the patient is presently taking – in thinking and talking about himself. These are the most important steps on that life journey.

A common misconception is that solution-focused therapists discourage any consideration of the past. The model is essentially patient led, and if the patient wishes to address issues concerning the past, the therapist will certainly do so. However, *how* this is undertaken will differ greatly from traditional psychotherapy. The solution-focused therapist will focus on:

▸ What the patient has learned from this past experience;

▸ What the patient wishes, now, to leave behind;

▸ How the patient would have liked to have been different in the past, and how that would have made a difference for the patient now;

▸ How the patient was able to live through or cope with past trauma, and where the patient gained the necessary resolve or support to do that.

The solution-focused therapist invariably takes a short break towards the end of the session. This serves as a clear signal to the patient that time is needed to reflect on what has been said, rather than serving up an immediate 'expert' summary. In Simon's (1996) view, all the techniques employed in SFT can be seen as a practice:

"… designed to induce in the therapist the attitude of respect for the client. From a position of respect, techniques per se become superfluous, as action appropriate to the situation is generated from the simple act of paying attention to what is needed" (ppo 53).

The therapist's respectful approach is represented by a kind of 'gentle curiosity', through which the therapist tries to get closer to an understanding of what is actually being said. Anderson and Goolishan (1992) described this as "a position of curiosity and not-yet-understanding". Adopting this view, the therapist's questions are *not* aimed at the usual list of therapist ambitions, such as: 'gathering information', 'making an assessment', 'testing a hypothesis', even 'being helpful' or 'trying to solve a problem'. Therapists *do not* ask questions if they already know the answers, and *do not* ask questions to get the patient to focus on something that the therapist already has in mind. Instead, the therapist's curiosity is aimed at establishing what *might* be created in this linguistic collaboration.

This approach recognises that the patient – like everyone else – is a story in the process of being told. Although we talk of a life lived in 'chapters', this is illusory, as there are no definitive beginning and end points to life, which flows through people. The therapist recognises that the patient's story is never ever complete and, for that reason, can never be fully understood. What is important is to recognise the *becoming* of the conversation (Walter and Peller, 1996). What takes place in the session is the unfolding of the patient's story, focused on the process, or the possibilities, of creating new meaning conjointly[12].

Homework assignments are also suggested after the break. These also respect the obvious fact that the session is only a small part of the patient's life. These assignments provide the patient with opportunities to notice change occurring, by small degrees, or otherwise to construct further their solutions in everyday life.

As noted at the outset, SFT challenges most of the accepted conventions of psychotherapy, especially the nature of the expert, all-knowing therapist, and the 'insightless', unknowing patient. It is often assumed, incorrectly, that SFT is appropriate only for patients with minor (or non-psychiatric) problems, or people who *want* to change. SFT has been used successfully with a wide range of life problems, including:

- Survivors of sexual abuse (Dolan, 1991);

- Domestic violence in relationships (Lipchik and Kubicki, 1996);

- In-patient hospital treatment (Webster et al, 1994;Vaughn et al, 1995).

DEALING WITH DIFFICULTY

Resistance is a psychoanalytic term, which has entered common psychotherapeutic parlance, to refer to patients who do not readily accept the therapist's support, or who otherwise do not respond to the therapist's help. Solution-focused therapists recognise the perjorative nature of this label, and, following Erickson's original tactic, view 'resistance' as the patient trying to give the therapist some help to be more effective O'Hanlon(1987).

'Resistance' most often occurs when the goals set by the patient conflict with the therapist's. *Resistance* is therefore a function of the difference between two different 'world views': that of the therapist – looking through his theoretical lens – and that of the patient and his 'lived experience'. When the therapist finds that something 'isn't working' he is more likely to apologise, or ask the client for more help to get the session 'back on target', rather than blame the patient's resistance.

Increasingly, the solution-focused literature describes work with people who did not come to therapy voluntarily. These *mandated* clients are manifestly 'resistant', in the traditional sense – they simply do not want to be helped, as the do not even recognise that they have a problem in the first place. These groups would include people sent by courts or probation services (in the case of offenders), protective agencies, schools or parents (in the case of children or adolescents) or employment programmes (Durrant, 1995); and individuals who are the focus of applications for case management (Van Dongen and Jambunathan, 1992). The solution-focused therapist does not try to encourage the client to 'accept' their problem, or otherwise 'recognise' it. The client's problem in these mandated scenarios is that he wants to be 'out' of therapy, and is obliged to be 'in' it. This *is* the client's problem and provides the basis for discussing what would be different if the authorities no longer wanted the person to be supervised, protected or whatever.

THE STRUCTURE OF THE SESSION

Despite the emphasis on an organic co-creation of the patient's story, most solution-focused therapists employ a structure that supports the growth of this lived story. The stages in the process of therapy are matched by the kind of questions asked, each of which suggests the therapist's philosophical standpoint: curious, respectful and willing to learn from the patient.

The therapist begins by asking *what* has brought the patient to therapy (the problem defined in the patient's own terms) and *how* the therapist might be able to help. From the outset, the therapist tries to establish what the patient sees as the problem and what any solution would achieve.

Little time is spent reviewing the problem – unless indicated by the patient – the focus at all times being on how things *will* be different, *after* the problem. Three specific methods are used to explore this future scenario:

▶ *The miracle question:* The patient is invited to imagine that a miracle occurs while he is asleep. "What is the first thing that you notice that tells you that the miracle has happened during the night?" The therapist then proceeds to ask for more detail and examples of *what* is different.

▶ *Relationship questions:* The patient is asked to describe what their partner, family, friends etc., would notice about him, after this miracle. "Who else would notice that a miracle had happened and what would *they* notice?" Where the patient is part of a family group, these questions are asked directly of the members.

▶ *Exception questions:* The therapist assumes that there are times when the problem isn't a problem: when the miracle has already happened, even to a limited degree. The therapist invites the patient to give examples of the times when the problem has not been evident, or has been much less in evidence. "What were you doing different then? What were other people doing different? What else was different?"

A fourth set of questions involve *scaling* the problem scenario, locating the patient (now) on a hypothetical scale (usually from 0 to 10, where 0 is the "worst" he has ever been and 10 is the "day after the miracle"). The patient may also be asked to describe "what would be different" at one point on the scale beyond the point where they presently stand. The therapist seeks as much detail about what 'is different' at that 'one step beyond'. Two further scales – using the same simple 0-to-10 dimensions – focus on:

▶ *Willingness:* "If 10 means you would do anything to solve this problem… and 0 means that you would just like to think about it… where do you stand right now?"

▶ *Confidence:* "If 10 means that you are very confident that you can solve this problem and 0 means that you think that you have no chance of solving this, where do you stand right now?"

Throughout, the therapist listens carefully to what the patient *actually* says, seeking clarification that he has heard correctly, inviting the patient to advise him if there is anything else that the patient wants to tell him.

The therapist takes a break, either to reflect privately on what has taken place, or to consult with colleagues who may have been viewing the session (with the patient's approval). On his return, the therapist always offers some validatory or complimentary message, thanking the patient for helping the therapist understand their situation, or acknowledging the complexity of his difficulties. Finally, the therapist makes a *bridging statement*, noting that because the patient said *this* or *that* the therapist would like to suggest a particular assignment.

Although the range of possible assignments is infinite, commonly they involve:

- *Noticing* when things are different in everyday life;

- *Predicting* whether or not the next day will be 'good' or 'bad';

- *Doing* something (anything) different;

- *Pretending* that things are different.

The selection of the assignment (or task) is geared specifically to what has been said in the session. In particular, the patient's scaling of willingness and confidence is important, as also is the existence of any concrete exceptions to the problem that might be developed. The therapist is also interested in the extent to which the patient feels in control of such exceptions (see Hawkes et al, 1998).

BRIEF BUT UNCERTAIN FUTURES?

Although the effectiveness of SFT, relative to other forms of therapy, remains unclear, there are indications that SFT is 'briefer' than most other therapies, and may demonstrate above average outcomes (De Jong and Hopwood, 1996). What is clear, however, is that by working with the patient's frame of reference, SFT may have a wider application across diverse patient groups. In mental health nursing, where respect for persons *and* social and cultural attachments is emphasised, SFT may have a particular relevance.

The idea of post-modern therapy, where a 'real reality' can never be known is, however, not without its problems, not least the implication that there can be no truth and, therefore, no lies (Held, 1995). Although this approach embodies an obvious pragmatism, it can generate intense hostility in traditional psychiatric thinkers, who believe that it is reckless to attempt to resolve problems *without* exploring their origins, or without some obvious theoretical basis. In that sense, SFT faces the same opposition that behaviour therapy encountered 50 years ago, in the opposition expressed by psychoanalysis.

However, the respectful, validating and empowering approach found in SFT may prove so attractive to a range of healthcare professionals – and their clientele – that sheer popularity and, hopefully, efficiency and effectiveness, will provide the support it needs to develop. In particular, these characteristics may provide mental health disciplines with a way to translate the rhetoric of holism and holistic care into a meaningful reality (Barker, 1996).

Footnotes

[10] I am conscious that many solution-focused therapists would not, given their philosophical position, describe themselves as psychotherapists. I use the term here merely for consistency.

[11] Again, the term 'patient' is employed for the sake of consistency.

[12] This storying approach is influenced greatly by the "narrative therapy" of White and Epston (1990).

References

Anderson, H. and Goolishan, H. (1992) *The Client is the expert: A not-knowing approach to therapy.* In S. McNamee and K.K. Gergen (eds) *Therapy as a Social Construction.* London: Sage.

Barker, P. (1996) *Solution-Focused Counseling: A new role for community psychiatric nurses as 'brief therapists'.* Report to the NHSE, National R&D Programme in Mental Health; Leeds, NHSE.

Bateson, G. (1979) *Mind and Nature: A necessary unity.* New York: Dutton.

Bateson, G., Jackson, D.D., Haley, J. and Weakland, J.H. (1956) Toward a theory of schizophrenia. *Behavioural Science; 1,* 251–264.

De Jong, P. and Hopwood, L.E. (1996) Outcome research on treatment conducted at the brief family therapy center, 1992-93. In S D Miller, M A Hubble and B L Duncan (eds) *Handbook of Solution-Focused Brief Therapy.* San Francisco: Jossey-Bass.

de Shazer, S. (1985) *Keys to Solutions in Brief Therapy.* New York: Norton.

de Shazer, S. (1988) *Clues: Investigating solutions in brief therapy.* New York: WW Norton.

de Shazer, S. (1991) *Putting Differences to Work.* New York: WW Norton.

de Shazer, S. (1993) Creative misunderstanding: There is no escape from language. In S. Gilligan and R. Price (Eds) *Therapeutic Conversations.* New York: WW Norton.

de Shazer, S. (1994) *Words were Originally Magic.* New York: WW Norton.

Dolan, Y. (1991) *Resolving Sexual Abuse: Solution-focused therapy and Ericksonian hypnosis for adult surivors.* New York: WW Norton.

Durrant, M. (1995) *Creative Strategies for School Problems.* New York: W.W. Norton.

Gergen, K. (1992) Toward a post-modern psychology. In S. Kvale (ed) *Psychology and Post-Modernism.* Newbury Park, California: Sage.

Harland, R. (1987) *Superstructuralism: The philosophy of structuralism and post structuralism.* London: Methuen.

Hawkes, D, Marsh, T.I. and Wilgosh, R (1998) *Solution Focused Therapy: A handbook for health care professionals.* Oxford: Butterworth Heinemann.

Held, B.S. (1995) *Back to Reality: A critique of post-modern theory in psychotherapy.* New York: W W Norton.

Lipchik, E. and Kubicki, A D (1996) Solution-focused domestic violence views: Bridges toward a new reality in couples therapy. In S D Miller, M.A. Hubble and B.L. Duncan (Eds) *Handbook of Solution-Focused Brief Therapy.* San Francisco: Jossey-Bass.

Mahoney, M.J. (1974) *Cognition and Behaviour Modification.* Cambridge Massachussetts: Ballinger.

Maturana, H. and Varela, F. (1987) *The Tree of Knowledge.* Boston: New Science Library.

Miller, S.D. (1995) Some questions (not answers) for the brief treatment of people with drug and alcohol problems. In M Hoyt (ed) *Constructive Therapies.* New York: Guilford.

Miller, S.D., Hubble, M.A. and Duncan B.L. (1996) *Handbook of Solution-Focused Brief Therapy.* San Francisco: Jossey-Bass.

O'Hanlon, W.H. (1987) *Taproots: Underlying Principle of Milton Erickson's Therapy and Hypnosis.* New York. Norton.

Simon, D. (1996) Crafting consciousness though form: Solution focused therapy as a spiritual path. In S.D. Miller, M.A. Hubble and B.L. Duncan (Eds) *Handbook of Solution Focused Brief Therapy*. San Francisco: Jossey-Bass.

Van Dongen, C.J. and Jambanathan, J. (1992) Pilot study results: The psychiatric RN case manager. *Journal of Psychosocial Nursing and Mental Health Services; 30 (11)*, 11-14, 35-36.

Vaughn, K., Webster D., Orahood, S. and Young, B. (1995) Brief inpatient psychiatric treatment: Finding solutions. *Issues in Mental Health Nursing; 16(6)*, 519-531.

Von Foerster, H. (1984) On constructing reality. In P. Watzlawick (Ed) *The Invented Reality. How do we know what we believe we know? Contributions to constructivism*. New York: W.W. Norton.

Von Glaserfeld, E. (1984) An introduction to radical constructivism. In P. Watzlawick (Ed) *The Invented Reality. How do we know what we believe we know? Contributions to constructivism*. New York: WW Norton.

Walter, J.L. and Peller, J.E. (1996) Rethinking our assumptions: Assuming anew in a post-modern world. In S.D. Miller, M.A. Hubble and B.L. Duncan (Eds) *Handbook of Solution-Focused Brief Therapy*. San Francisco: Jossey-Bass.

Watts, A. (1961) *Psychotherapy East and West*. New York: Pantheon Books.

Watzlawick, P. (1978) *The Language of Change*. New York: Basic Books.

Watzlawick, P. (1984) *The Invented Reality: How do we know what we believe we know? Contributions to constructivism*. New York: W.W. Norton.

Watzlawick, P., Weakland, J. and Fisch, R. (1974) *Change*. New York: W.W. Norton.

Weakland, J., Fisch R., Watzlawick, P. and Bodin, A. (1974) Brief therapy: Focused problem resolution. *Family Process; 13*, 141–168.

Webster, D., Vaughn, K. and Martinez, R. (1994) Introducing solution-focused approaches to staff in inpatient psychiatric setting. *Archives of Psychiatric Nursing; 8(4)*, 254–561.

White, M. and Epston, D. (1990) *Narrative Means to Therapeutic Ends*. New York: Norton.

Winnicott, D.W. (1971) *Playing and Reality*. London: Tavistock Publications.

Wittgenstein, L. (1958) *Philosophical Investigations*. London: Macmillan.

Case study 9

A SOLUTION-FOCUSED APPROACH TO SELF-HARM

Ron Wilgosh

Jenny was referred for counselling by a GP after she had presented to him stating that she felt depressed, was experiencing panic attacks and was self-harming by cutting her thighs. She is 17 years old.

Therapist: So, what's brought you here to see me today, Jenny?

Jenny: I went to see my doctor and he suggested it.

T: What was it about your conversation together, do you suppose, that led him to think going for counselling will help?

J: Well, I went to see him because I'm not getting on with my life very well. I just feel useless and I cry all the time. I've stopped going out because I get embarrassed. It's stupid, I know, but I get frightened and flustered and feel like I'm making a fool of myself.

T: This sounds quite difficult for you. What helps you to cope with it?

J: I don't really. Like I say, I cry… and this is embarrassing, but I cut myself.

T: What do you mean?

J: When I feel low and frustrated, I cut my legs. My thighs, where no one can see. They're covered in really bad cuts and I want to stop doing it.

T: How does that help, cutting your legs?

J: It doesn't really, not in the long run. I feel guilty. But it makes me feel better at the time.

T: Do those thoughts of hurting yourself ever get worse? Do you ever think of seriously harming yourself?

J: Sometimes. I've thought about killing myself... but I don't want to do that. It frightens me.

T: You want to find a better way of sorting this out?

J: Oh yeah. I've got to.

T: You know Jenny, when people get a problem, they tend to think about it and how come it's happened to them. What ideas do you have about why this has happened to you?

J: I know why it's happened to me. It's because my mum and dad split up three years ago. I was fine until then. But when my dad left, my mum didn't cope very well. He went off with another woman and mum fell to pieces. She cried all the time and didn't look after herself. I was really worried about her.

T: You talk about it in the past tense. It's not like that now?

J: No. My mum's not. She's coping better now, but it's hard because I don't see my dad now. I mean, I see him because he still lives nearby, but when I see him in town, he just ignores me now.

T: That must hurt. How do you handle that?

J: Well, that's why I cry, I think, and hurt myself.

T: So that's how you've been handling it up 'til now, but you want to change that?

J: Yeah.

T: Is there anything else, Jenny, that you think I need to know about?

J: Only that I'm due to sit my exams at college soon and I'm not confident about that. And I don't know what I want to do when I leave. And my boyfriend's going off to University in September. That upsets me.

T: You're going to miss him?

J: Oh yes. He gives me a lot of confidence. He encourages me.

T: Is there anything else?

J: No, I don't think so.

T: How would you like counselling to help you with this?

J: I don't know really. I need to sort this out. I suppose if you could help me to stop feeling like this, that would help a lot.

T: How Jenny? If you could stop feeling like this, what difference would that make?

J: I could get back to normal. Start living my life again. Feel happy. Stuff like that.

T: Okay. Well, let me ask you a strange question Jenny. One that requires quite a bit of imagination. Imagine that when you go from here today and tonight when you go to bed a miracle happens for you. The outcome of this miracle is that the problems that you came here with today have gone. Just like that. But, because you're asleep, you don't know a miracle has happened. When you wake up tomorrow morning, what will be the first thing that you will discover that will tell you those problems have gone?

J: When I first wake up?

T: Yes.

J: I won't be feeling nervous anymore. This horrible feeling in my stomach.

T: Okay, so when you're not feeling nervous anymore, how will you be feeling instead?

J: Confident. Ready to get on with things.

T: Tell me more about feeling confident. What will it look like?

J: I'll start going out more... with my friends, even on my own. I'll go to clubs with my boyfriend, because I've been making excuses for a long time.

T: What else will tell you that you're confident?

J: I won't let my dad bother me so much, and I guess I'll have some idea of what I'm going to do after I leave college.

T: How will this help you, Jenny, when you start behaving this way?

J: Well, it's the old me. If I can get that back, then I think I'm getting there.

T: Okay. Coming back to this miracle. What else will tell you that a miracle has happened?

J: I won't be cutting, obviously.

T: What difference will that make to you?

J: Well, I feel like I'm weird, you know, abnormal for doing it.

T: So, when you stop, that will make you feel normal again?

J: Yeah.

T: What difference will that make to you, feeling normal again?

J: Well, that's another sign that I'm getting over this and getting my life back together again.

T: So, when you stop cutting, what will you do instead when you feel frustrated or low?

J: Tough one.

T: Yes, it is.

J: I could talk more about how I'm feeling.

T: You'll be talking more instead. Who to?

J: My boyfriend. I shut him out and he gets angry about that. He really cares about me.

T: Anyone else?

J: My mum. She worries about me a lot. She knows when I'm down. She doesn't know I cut, through. And my best friend. I think she would understand.

T: And how will talking to these people help you, Jenny?

J: It will take some of the pressure off. It will mean I won't have to carry all this stuff around.

T: What difference will that make to you?

J: If I can get rid of some of these bad feelings, I think that will help me to feel better. It'll make me feel more worthwhile, too, if I share what I'm feeling with people. It'll be hard though. I don't know if I can do it. This is the most I've ever talked to anyone about my problems.

T: Really. So, by talking to me here today, you've really taken a big step towards looking after yourself?

J: I hadn't though about it like that, but yeah, a big step.

T: Was it hard or did you know you could do this?

J: No, it was hard.

T: Congratulations.

J: Thank you.

T: What has this taught you about yourself? What have you discovered?

J: That I'm stronger than I thought I was.

T: Really? You've learnt that you're stronger than you believed you were?

J: Yeah. I'm surprised at how much I've talked here.

T: What else will tell you a miracle has happened?

J: I want to confront my dad.

T: How do you want to do that?

J: I can't talk to him to his face because that'll upset me, and he's always with his girlfriend anyway.

T: So, how will you do it?

J: I thought of writing to him and telling him how I feel.

T: Do you want him to know anything else?

J: I want to ask him why he ignores me. It really hurts and I get so angry with him and I want him to know that.

T: Sounds like you miss him.

J: I do miss him.

T: Do you still love him?

J: Yeah, I do.

T: Do you have any thoughts, Jenny, about why he behaves as he does?

J: Guilt. I think he feels guilty about what he's done to mum and about leaving me. But I'm not sure.

T: And how will writing to him help you?

J: I want to clear the air. I need to know why he's done what he has and I want us to be able to stay in contact.

T: Difficult question, Jenny, but what if he doesn't want that?

J: Well, at least I've got things off my chest. That will help me. I feel used by him at the moment, and I'm not going to allow that.

T: Wow.

J: I know. I just shocked myself. I didn't believe I could say that.

T: It sounds like you're already becoming stronger and taking control of your life.

J: Yeah, I guess so.

T: How will your mum know that a miracle has happened for you? If you didn't tell her, what will she notice?

J: I'll spend more time with her and talk to her more.

T: What else?

J: She'll see me laughing more and going out without worrying about it.

T: So, when your mum sees you spending more time with her, talking to her more, laughing more and being more confident, what difference will that make to her?

J: I'll think she'll be able to relax. She's always watching me or asking me how I am. I know she worries and it hurts her when I shut myself off.

T: When she relaxes more and doesn't need to worry so much, how will that affect you?

J: I'll be more relaxed too. We'll have more fun together. I used to get on really well with mum before all of this.

T: Will she notice anything else?

J: No, that's about it.

T: What about your boyfriend? How will he know that a miracle's happened for you?

J: That's easy. I'll be going out more with him instead of making excuses if it involved going where there's crowds.

T: Okay, and what else?

J: He'll know that I've stopped cutting, obviously, because he'll be able to see, and I'll talk about my problems with him more.

T: When he notices all of these things, how will he react, do you suppose?

J: He'll be delighted. Not just about the going out, but when he knows I've stopped cutting, he'll be relieved. I think he was frightened about what I was going to do next, and I think that talking more about myself will bring us closer. I mean, we're close already, but he'll know stuff about me that I haven't said before, except for here.

T: Will he notice anything else, do you suppose?

J: I'm frightened about him going away in September and what that might do to us, and because I'm worried, I become distant. So, it'll be hard, but we need to talk about that.

T: What about your friends, Jenny? What will they notice?

J: They'll see more of me for a start. I'll be the happy, game-for-anything Jenny they used to know. They'll see me being more confident and talking more.

T: Are there times already, Jenny, when parts of this miracle are happening already, even in a small way?

J: Well, yeah. There are times when I'm more like my old self, especially with my mum.

T: Really. How do you get that to happen?

J: I don't know really.

T: Are you sure? You can't think what it is that you're doing or what's happening?

J: Er, no.

T: So, you're obviously doing something that's working, even though you can't put your finger on it yet?

J: I must be.

T: Any other times when this miracle is happening?

J: Well, yeah. I can go out to the shops occasionally, and I go out with my boyfriend, of course.

T: How do you get yourself to do these things?

J: I dunno. I think some days I just feel more confident than others. I'm not sure.

T: What's different, do you suppose, on those confident days?

J: I must be thinking differently. Some days I like myself more. I look at what I've achieved and what I'm doing and what I've got, and it helps me to feel more positive.

T: Really. How can you make that happen more often?

J: I don't know if I can. I have to remind myself of my good points, I guess. Even though I've got these problems, it's not all bad.

T: Okay. I'm going to ask you a scaling question now. On a scale of 0 to 10, where 10 is the day after the miracle and 0 is the worst this problem has been, where are you at this moment?

J: About a 3

T: You're at a 3?

J: Yeah.

T: Can you remember a time when you were at 0?

J: Oh yeah, it wasn't long ago.

T: So how, Jenny, did you move from 0 to 3?

J: I'm not sure. I'm thinking differently, I think. I got good grades in my mocks, so even though I'm not confident about them, my marks suggest I'm doing OK.

T: So, if you're at a 3 at the moment, what will tell you that you've moved to 4? Just a small step further on.

J: If I stop cutting myself

T: Really. That sounds to me like it will be nearer 6 or 7, when you've stopped cutting yourself.

J: Yeah. I think you're right. I think a 4 will be when I'm talking more about my worries to people.

T: What else?

J: When I'm feeling more confident.

T: How will you know that?

J: I'll be going out more often, with my friends.

T: Alright. Another scaling question now. Where are you on a scale of 0 to 10, if 0 is all that you're prepared to do is hope and pray that this problem goes away and 10 is that you will do anything that you think will help with this problem?

J: 10, definitely. I've got to do something. I've had enough of it.

T: 10? You really want to beat this?

J: Yes. I do.

T: How confident are you, say on a scale of 0 to 10, where 0 is you're not at all confident and 10 is that you have every confidence you're going to beat this?

J: About a 6 or 7, because it's not all in my control. I don't know how my dad will react, and I don't know what will happen to my boyfriend and me once he leaves, so I'm not entirely confident that I can make it all happen.

T: Is there anything else, Jenny, that I haven't asked you about or that you think is important and I need to know? Or is there anything else you want to ask me?

J: Er, no. I think I've said everything that's important to me. I can't believe I've talked so much. I wasn't sure what I was going to say to you when I came here.

T: Well, I'm just going to take a short break now, to think about our conversation, Jenny, and I'll come back in about five minutes and share my thoughts with you. Okay?

J: Yeah, fine.

Break

T: I'd like to thank you for coming along and talking with me today, Jenny. It's helped me to begin to understand how things are for you, and I think you were wise to make the decision to sort your life out. I appreciate how difficult it can be talking to someone for the first time about your problems, and doing so must have taken some courage on your part. I'm impressed with how honest you've been. I'm also impressed with how you are already beginning to deal with what are very difficult and painful circumstances for you. I heard how hurtful your father's behaviour is for you. Even though you still find that difficult to deal with, somehow you have a capacity to grow from that experience. You haven't allowed what he's done to cloud how you feel about him, and, in fact, you've become stronger, which is reflected in your decision to confront him and let him know that you won't tolerate him treating you this way. I'm also struck by your determination to treat your feelings with greater respect and, instead of continuing to hurt yourself, you intend to be more open and honest about how you feel and to share this with people that really matter to you. Even though you acknowledge it will be hard work for you, you also recognise that it is a way of handling your feelings that seems more appropriate and, in your terms, 'normal' to you. The fact that you are at 10 in terms of wanting to sort your life out – I would like to suggest that you pay attention to everything you do that you consider to be a sign of you sorting your life out and observe how that helps you to move from 4 to 5 or even higher on your scale. We'll talk about what you've discovered about yourself some more next time. Okay?

J: Yeah, fine. Thank you very much. That was helpful.

T: When do you think it will be helpful for us to meet again, Jenny?

J: Er, about three weeks. Is that okay?

Session 2

T: So, what's been better, even in a small way?

J: Well, I haven't cut myself since my last appointment.

T: What! How have you done that?

J: I know. I surprised myself. But I haven't felt the need to cut.

T: How come? What have you been doing right?

J: Well, I did what I said. When I left here, I went home and wrote a letter to my dad, saying all the things that I wanted him to know.

T: Really! How did that help?

J: It was such a relief. Just to vent all that stuff. Just writing it helped a lot. But, I posted it as well, and he wrote back and he wants to meet me.

T: How do you feel about that?

J: I'm delighted. A little nervous, but he can't frighten me now. I've already told him how I feel.

T: That must have taken a lot of courage.

J: It did. But it makes me feel good too.

T: So, what else is better?

J: Well, I'm talking about my feelings now. I told my mum and she was so relieved to finally know what was happening with me. And we've carried on. She's been brilliant.

T: What else?

J: Well, you know I said I was worried about my relationship with my boyfriend and I wanted to tell him?

T: Yes.

J: Well, I did. I explained how frightened I was for us, and he said he had been feeling the same, so we decided to get engaged – on my birthday.

T: Congratulations! That's wonderful.

J: Thank you. It's made such a difference, getting this off my chest. I didn't believe I would feel like this so quickly. I feel brilliant and in control. Before, I felt I couldn't do anything to change things, but I can. I feel a lot more confident…

T: Like your 'old' self?

J: Getting there. I'm close, but I'm being cautious. I don't want to ruin it.

T: So, where would you say you are on that 0 to 10 scale today?

J: 6, definitely a 6.

I continued to explore what else Jenny had achieved, what this meant to her and, more importantly, how it had positively affected her view of herself. We discussed what she needed to do to maintain her progress, and what else she wanted to achieve for herself in therapy.

At her request, I saw her on two further occasions as she consolidated these changes, had her first meeting with her father, and worked out what she wanted to do with her future after college.

Case study 10

A SOLUTION-FOCUSED APPROACH TO RELATIONSHIPS AND VIOLENCE

Kay Vaughn, Denise Webster and Cordt Kassner

The following case illustrates a typical initial intake, the first three sessions, and a follow-up session for a couple referred for marital counselling following a domestic violence incident. The "framing of goals" is representative of what we have experienced in domestic violence cases.

Gary and Dana have been married for 15 years and have three teenage children. Gary's position as a mail carrier has become increasingly stressful, and that strain has added friction to their already volatile relationship. Dana works fulltime as a cosmetic salesperson, and has been having difficulty handling their eldest son, Jedd. Gary acknowledges that he currently feels depressed, but is reluctant to take any medications. Last year, he took an antidepressant medication for six months, but stopped it due to side effects. Recently, for the first time in their marriage, Gary struck his wife.

Initial intake

Prior to the first session, the couples' nurse therapist conducted an initial telephone intake. There are two purposes of the initial intake in domestic violence therapy. First, information is gathered to better understand why therapy is being requested. Second, specific history is obtained to complete a safety risk assessment for the couple. It is important to note that discussion about the rationale for therapy ('the problem') occurs prior to, not during, the first therapy session.

First session

Emphasis during the first session is placed on finding solutions to problems. Goal clarification and identification of exceptions to problems are also discussed.

Therapist: This may sound like an unusual question to start off with, but when the problem you currently have is resolved, how will you know you no longer need to come back?

Gary: We need to learn better communication skills. For example, giving direct feedback to each other.

Dana: I agree. Also, Gary has to stop bringing up past arguments out of nowhere.

G: We need to be on the same page more often, you know, talking about the same thing.

Because the goal is vague, the therapist decides to use the miracle question to get specific information about the couple's goals.

T: Pretend that tonight when you go to sleep, a miracle occurs. Somehow, magically, when you both wake, up you are able to communicate more clearly with each other. However, you were asleep and didn't know this miracle happened. What is the first thing each of you will notice to recognise that this miracle occurred?

G: That's easy for me – I won't have to constantly clarify what she means. Right now she only tells me part of a problem she has, so I have to keep begging for more information to help her make a decision.

D: When the miracle happens for me, Gary will say, "I thought you said...", instead of assuming what I meant and getting angry.

At this time, the therapist asks for recent exceptions to the problems.

T: Since we talked on the phone, describe one time when you have communicated well.

D: Actually, we did have a recent situation where we dealt with Jedd better than we usually do. We put Jedd on a behavioural contract because of fighting at school, but he is always arguing with me about it. Last week, Jedd got into another fight, but this time Gary and I discussed the situation and decided together what his consequences would be. We presented the consequences together, so that Jedd couldn't play us off each other.

T: Terrific! Can you think of another time when you have been able to discuss and agree on decisions together?

G: We used to be able to do that a lot.

D: There used to be much less stress. However, even when it was stressful, things seemed to go better when Gary was taking medication.

G: There has been more stress lately. At first, it seemed to be mostly at work, but now I can't seem to get along with anyone. There is tension at work, and then I come home to Dana and Jedd fighting over something. I feel really guilty –I never hit Dana before last week – but I can't seem to control my temper these days.

We often link safety to client-identified goals, if safety is not mentioned in cases involving domestic violence.

T: I'm going to ask you a numerical question. On a scale of 1 to 10, I want each of you to individually rank how safe communication is in your home. With 1 being "I don't say a word because I don't feel safe to talk" and 10 being "I can safely say anything and know I will be treated with respect", how safe is your communication right now?

D: I don't want to make you angry, Gary, but since you have stopped your medication and had such mood swings, I am about a 2. His rages have really made me afraid and I have withdrawn a lot.

G: I am about a 5. I haven't felt safe lately because I don't know who I am anymore. I can't control my feelings. I'm afraid she may leave me, and I'm afraid of what that would be like.

T: What would it take for each of you to move up one point on the safety scale?

Each agreed that listening better would help them feel safer.

A homework assignment was given to notice the times when they were listening better.

Second session

T: What has improved?

G: Since last session, I've noticed Dana working at communicating. I feel more willing to hear what she is saying without suspecting ulterior motives. Her communication is clearer and she's been less demanding.

T: What is she doing instead?

G: Now she is requesting, rather than demanding, my attention: it feels more like co-operation. It is a subtle change, but I feel more relaxed.

T: What else has changed?

G: It feels like we are working together to accomplish a task, instead of one demanding that the other participate.

D: Things were much smoother. Gary is less agitated over what I say. For example, when I call the kids by the wrong name, he doesn't correct me and question what I really meant. He is also more attentive. He took me out on Valentine's Day.

T: That is a lot of change. How did you do all of that?

G: The discussion last week helped us to better understand each other. Also, I started back on medication and I feel more relaxed. I guess I've been overreacting. I feel less pressured now, and closer to Dana.

T: Did the two of you do anything else together?

D: One night we went to dinner and a movie, but neither of us liked the movie. In the past, we would have fought about who chose the movie, but this time no one got blamed for it.

T: Have the kids noticed anything different about your communication?

D: They've noticed we are working together more like a team. Jedd is the most reactive, and he has been really good lately.

T: What difference does it make in your relationship when your kids see you communicating better and working together as a team?

G: I think the kids notice there is less stress and hostility. Our daughter Katie has been more affectionate with me since I started medication. I don't feel so pressured, and I'm actually driving more safely now.

T: Do you both remember the scale we used last session? How would you scale your communication safety this week?

D: I am a 5 or 6.

G: I am a 6 or 7.

T: Both of you have made improvement. What will it take for each of you to move even one number higher?

G: Because everything has been so stressful at work, I would like to have more casual conversations at home - for example, about the weather or news.

D: I would still prefer that he ask how I feel instead of him telling me how I feel, but he has been doing better.

T: How have the improvements Gary has made so far made a difference for you?

D: When he is not so stressed, there is less tension at home, so I calm down and can speak more clearly.

T: Scale your confidence that you can continue to communicate better if Gary stays on his medication.

D: 8.

G: I am not concerned about confidence. I just have to take it one day at a time. I can't promise I will never lose my temper again, but I am trying to be more relaxed.

T: How will Dana know that you are taking it one day at a time and trying to stay relaxed?

G: Well, she will see I am taking better care of myself by going for walks to relax and not jumping to conclusions.

T: How do you do that – "not jumping to conclusions"?

G: I remember when I was a kid, my mother told me to count to 10 and take a deep breath before you say anything. I have been doing that, and it really helps.

T: What else are you doing to relax and take care of yourself?

G: Well, walking is restful when I am not doing it for my job. I like to walk out in the country on weekends. I used to go fishing to relax and I haven't done that for a long time. I have been thinking about going fishing, and maybe taking Jedd with me next time. I think it would be good if Dana got out of the house more, too.

T: I was just going to ask Dana, what do you do to take care of yourself?

D: I've been thinking about that myself. It has been a long time since I've spent time with any of my friends. It always seemed to upset Gary if I went anywhere. I really miss just being with the girls sometimes. Maybe Elaine and I could take the exercise class down in the community centre. I used to do that and it made a big difference.

T: Are there things you would be willing to do together to take care of your relationship?

D: After this session we are going out to dinner.

G: We talked about having a standing date again, like we did when we were first married.

T: What is the likelihood that you will be doing these things to take care of yourselves and your relationship, before our next session?

G: I think there is a pretty good chance.

D: I would need to know that it is okay with him if I spend time with my friends – that I won't hear about it later.

G: As long as we have agreed about who is going to take care of the kids, no problem.

A homework assignment was given to notice what difference it makes for each of them when effort is made to communicate more clearly, to work more like a team, and to do things necessary to take care of both themselves and their relationship.

Third session

T: How is it going?

G: We are communicating much better and having more open discussions.

D: There is much less hostility now.

G: She is making more requests. There is a change in how she says things. So now I am more relaxed and friendly.

T: So you have continued to communicate better. What differences have you noticed, since you have done that for more than a month now?

G: I feel more included in decisions, rather than being told what to do. I feel part of the family. I feel like we are co-operating.

D: He is much easier going now. He has really changed.

T: If I were watching a video of this new co-operation, what would I see?

D: We spend more time together.

G: I don't isolate or dwell on the past anymore. I spend more relaxed time with the kids.

D: That's true. He's not isolating.

T: If the kids were here now, what would they say?

G: Actually, someone from the office called yesterday and spoke with Jedd. She commented on how mature and helpful Jedd was.

D: Katie notices Dad's driving the most – she said that he doesn't drive crazy anymore.

G: I think Katie is much less hostile and moody.

T: That is really amazing! What have you done as parents to raise such co-operative adolescents?

G: We taught them to be independent and identify what their options are.

D: Co-operation has always been really important in our family. That's why it was so disturbing when we weren't getting along.

T: You have been communicating better for a while now. How confident are you that you can continue in the direction you have been going? On a scale of 1 to 10?

D: I'm an 8, but I would have difficulty staying confident if he doesn't continue taking his medication. I am not convinced he wants to continue taking his medication.

G: You're right, I don't want to take it forever. I want to be able to control my temper without medications.

T: It is usually not necessary to stay on these medications for long periods of time. That's something we may want to evaluate when you are feeling confident that your other approaches to relaxation are working well. How are each of you doing with your self-care plans?

G: I actually went fishing last week. I haven't taken Jedd yet, but he's thinking about going with me. He's at the age when he'd rather spend time with his friends.

D: I had tea with an old girlfriend last week, and I started looking for an exercise class that would work with my schedule.

T: What difference does it make to your relationship, when each of you is doing the things you need to do to relax?

D: All the difference in the world. I don't feel like a prisoner in my own home.

G: I think it's made a big difference for both of us. I'm not nearly as tense and I don't fly off the handle like I used to.

T: How could Dana feel more confident about your decisions whether or not to take your medication, and how long you take it?

G: I think we will talk about it like we have the other problems, and it is a decision we will make together as a team.

Follow-up session

Gary and Dana were seen at their request two months later and then again three months later, for what they called their "check-up". Despite the usual stresses of family and work, they both agreed those things are much better for them and they are willing to do a trial period without medication in five more months. They are confident that they can do whatever it takes to maintain safety in their relationship.

Epilogue

Phil Barker

The five approaches to psychotherapy illustrated here are, as noted in the introduction, only a small proportion of a growing band of therapies. This growth in the therapies industry is clearly a function of the market. Therapists sell workshops, courses, books and tapes. A new therapy means a new niche in the market. This growth has not been without its detractors, and psychotherapy now has a bigger queue of critics than ever before in its history. They include those who continue to challenge the scientific basis of therapy, asking for evidence for its utility, especially if it is to be provided from state or insurance company funds. The queue also includes those who say that therapy is abusive and damaging, either weakening people further or actually implanting ideas about problems, as in the notion of "false memory syndrome". Despite these attacks, therapy appears to be prospering – but what will the future bring?

One of the enduring characteristics of psychotherapy is the factionalism, and often open warfare, that goes on between different schools of thought. All five schools illustrated in this book are different from one another, sometimes in obvious ways, sometimes more subtly. Whether any one approach is *better* than another is open to question. The famous meta-analysis of psychotherapy literature conducted by Smith, Glass and Miller in 1980 showed that all forms of therapy were equally effective: all had won and all must have prizes! Despite such evidence, different schools still compete, perhaps inspired as much by ideology and corporate identity, as financial gain. Most therapeutic approaches are useful, but advocates invariably try to exclude everything but their own model. Once there was only psychoanalysis, and then along came the behavioural, humanistic, family and solution-focused approaches, each showing how useful an 'alternative' approach might be. Regrettably, many of the advocates of these approaches get carried away with their own importance, acting as if

God had handed down their model on a new tablet of stone. When followers group around a school or approach, they invariably develop deep attachments to one another, as well as to the model that holds them together. In time, the simple utility of the approach can be forgotten, and ever more complex theories are generated, and a whole world of publishing – research, theorising and polemic – opens up, flooding the market with material that few – except the cognoscenti - can understand. The practice of most forms of therapy is simple, as the illustrations offered in this book illustrate. However, most schools have rendered their models complex, and increasingly claim the need for extensive training before anyone is considered competent to practise. This notion of a guild right to practise is also a function of the market place, but is one that may be therapy's undoing.

Increasingly, it is being argued that 'what works' in therapy does not belong to any one school of thought, but can be found in many. Griffin and Tyrrell (1998) have called these characteristics the "human givens". Therapy always works best when it comes from a real understanding of the what it means to be human, rather than from a narrow theoretical or emotional viewpoint. Among the 'human givens' they list as central to effective therapeutic practice are the following:

- The brain can experience itself – awareness is the "observing self";

- Strong emotions produce trance states that can inhibit the thinking part of the brain;

- People are programmed to employ metaphor in dreams and thinking as an aid to understanding;

- Imagination can be made to work for or against us;

- People search for meaning – without meaning they suffer boredom and despair;

- Some degree of control over life is a necessary part of functioning;

- People need attention;

- They also need to be part of a community;

- The mind and the body are not separate but are a united whole.

Given these 'human givens', it seems clear that a new kind of psychotherapy (which has been termed "transpersonal") might rise to prominence in the 21st century. Such an approach will have no truck with factionalism, and will value the opening, rather than closing, of minds, that has often been the psychotherapeutic case to date. An approach to therapy that values the 'human givens' will offer opportunities not only to resolve the distress that people experience but also promises to empower the person through raised awareness and true 'personal wisdom'. Such gains may well return psychotherapy to the spiritual domain from which it first sprung: addressing the wholeness of experience, including humankind's experience of the infinite. The healing of the mind envisaged by the ancient Greeks has had a long and chequered career. It is a story without an ending. Perhaps the best part is yet to come.

References

Smith, M.L., Glass, G.V. and Miller, J.L. (1980) *The Benefits of Psychotherapy.* Baltimore: John Hopkins.

Griffin, J. and Tyrrell, I. (1998) The 'human givens'. *The Therapist; 5 (1)*, 24–29 .

Index